Hockey Fitness
Year-Round Conditioning On and Off the Ice

Don MacAdam, MPE
Edmonton Oilers Development Team
Head Coach

Gail Reynolds, MA

Leisure Press
Champaign, Illinois

Developmental Editor: June I. Decker, PhD
Copy Editor: Wendy Nelson
Assistant Editor: JoAnne Cline
Production Director: Ernie Noa
Projects Manager: Lezli Harris
Typesetter: Brad Colson
Text Design: Keith Blomberg
Text Layout: Michelle Baum
Cover Design: Conundrum Designs
Cover Photo: David Klutho/Focus West
Illustrations By: Beverly Romanchuk
Printed By: Versa Press

ISBN: 0-88011-314-6

Copyright © 1988 by Don MacAdam and Gail Reynolds

Library of Congress Cataloging-in-Publication Data

MacAdam, Don, 1950-
    Hockey fitness.

    Bibliography: p.
    Includes index.
    1. Hockey—Training.   2. Physical education and training.   I. Reynolds, Gail, 1949-   II. Title.
GV848.3.M33 1988   796.96'2'07   88-681
ISBN 0-88011-314-6

Printed in the United States of America

10 9 8 7 6 5 4 3

Leisure Press
A Division of Human Kinetics
  Publishers, Inc.
Box 5076, Champaign, IL 61825-5076
1-800-747-4457

Canada Office:
Human Kinetics Publishers, Inc.
P.O. Box 2503, Windsor, ON N8Y 4S2
1-800-465-7301 (in Canada only)

Europe Office:
Human Kinetics Publishers (Europe) Ltd.
P.O. Box IW14
Leeds LS16 6TR
England
0532-781708

Dedication

To John Meagher and Lyman MacInnis for their words of wisdom.

Contents

Foreword

I have coached players from Midget to National Hockey League levels over the past 20 years. I've been fortunate to have a lot of success, and I believe that success is based on one thing—hard work. Conditioning is the cornerstone of hard work in hockey. You can't practice hard or play hard if you're not in good shape.

I have used MacAdam's and Reynolds' conditioning programs since 1981—I know they work. Players who show discipline in their conditioning show discipline in their playing. That's what makes the successful player and the successful team.

Hockey Fitness is an excellent guide for coaches and players of any age who are serious about conditioning. Players need the right exercise, proper rest, and good eating habits to perform their best. It's all there in *Hockey Fitness*. The book is full of practical drills and ideas. And it's written so that everything is easy to understand.

It is unacceptable for today's hockey player to be in poor condition. *Hockey Fitness* is a clear way to get and stay in good shape.

Jacques Demers
Coach, Detroit Red Wings

Acknowledgments

Thanks first to the players and teams at the University of New Brunswick who have enthusiastically subjected themselves to our training experiments year after year as we perfected the conditioning programs presented in this book. Thanks to subsequent amateur, Junior, and NHL players who helped establish that these techniques work at all levels. A special thanks to Jacques Demers, coach of the Detroit Red Wings, for showing his confidence in these programs. And thanks to the many hockey coaches who used our programs and returned constructive commentary on different aspects of our works.

Special thanks goes to the Detroit Red Wings organization, to Jim Lites, executive vice-president, and to Bill Jamieson, director of public relations, for providing Red Wings photographs and granting us permission to use them in the book.

Also, thanks to John Hartman for his photographs and Bev Romanchuk for her illustrations.

INTRODUCTION

The Hockey Conditioning Connection

Hockey: the game of strength, speed, and finesse. Conditioning: the number-one fatigue fighter. Fatigue: the easiest way to render strength, speed, and finesse ineffective. That is the hockey conditioning connection. If a hockey player can postpone fatigue until after the game, he can perform at his best strength, speed, and ability all through his game. What better way to play hockey?

Athletes have been using conditioning for centuries to help them perform better at their sports. Sprinters run miles, shot-putters do weight training, and figure skaters work on their flexibility. As a result, world records tumble and performances become nearly perfect.

But what can athletes do to condition themselves for a sport like hockey that involves such a diversity of movements and skills? Players have to skate and hit and shoot, and get both in and out of the path of other players. Hockey calls on the body to give and take in a tremendous variety of ways.

A hockey player's body is made up of bones that are manipulated by muscles that are fed by miles of blood vessels and follow instructions dictated by chains of nerve cells. All these parts must work together. The beauty of this whole network is that it is very versatile; the body can adapt to all sorts of situations. If you constantly practice in a hot rink, your body will get better at performing in the heat. If now you exercise your body 5 days a week when last year you only exercised twice a week, your body gets better at handling 5 days of exercise in a row. If you previously skated at three-quarter speed most of the time and you decide to practice frequently at full speed, your body gets better at going at full speed.

Bones, muscles, heart, blood vessels, nerves, and even chemicals in your body adapt to handle the job better if they are given the work repeatedly. That is how conditioning lets a hockey player's body act stronger, faster, longer, and more efficiently. What does that do to his game?

The stronger a player gets, the harder he can shoot and the harder he can push off against the ice to skate. He can keep the opposition under control more easily when trying to skate them out of position or knock their sticks off the puck. He will also be able to hold his own position more easily, as when trying to control the front of the net.

The faster hockey player has a constant edge. He can get to the puck and away with the puck more often without being stopped. He can get shots away before being checked, and he is more likely to get clear of his check so he can stay in play.

The player who develops his endurance is the one who gets to use his skills, speed, and strength at their peak through all 20 minutes of all three periods. He doesn't fade at the end of periods or games, when his skills and speed are most needed. Overtime becomes something to look forward to winning.

The efficient player makes easy movements that don't strain his joints or muscles so that he can get more power out of his movements, and he is at less risk of injury. Efficiency also extends to his nerves. They can take advantage of opportunities, like the forward who sees an opening on goal and can process the message quickly enough to fire a shot. When the shot is sent off with no hesitation, the goaltender has no time to set up.

Conditioning is a way of life for any serious hockey player. It allows him to play to the best of his ability and to do so as long as he pleases. Fatigue never inhibits his skills or strategies. He can use his strength, speed, and finesse through the entire game. How does he get to that level of conditioning?

Part I of *Hockey Fitness* explains the theory behind proper conditioning so coaches and serious players can understand why so much is possible.

Part II presents principles for ensuring proper conditioning and provides sample drills to illustrate those principles. Following each

drill recommendations are made for modifying the drill to suit
various levels of players. Level 1 is for young, inexperienced, and/or
poorly conditioned hockey players whose skills are very average
to weak. Level 2 modifications are for moderately skilled and experienced players who want to play the game safely and well. This
would include most players 12 to 16 years of age, some young, elite
players, and most "old timers" who are returning to the game for
a recreational activity. Level 3 is for skilled, serious, experienced
players, usually 17 years of age and up, including junior, college,
and very active old timers. Level 2 should often be used as a
stepping-stone for Level 3 exercises. Coaches can use the principles
and sample drills of Part II as guides for designing their own conditioning drills.

Part III is a guide to evaluation and incorporation of conditioning into your own hockey program.

The information in *Hockey Fitness* is presented so that it can be
applied to mites, midgets, professional, and old timer hockey
players. Precautions for different ages and levels of development
are discussed where appropriate. The information is also applicable
to both male and female hockey players. Reference throughout the
text, however, is to the male gender because presently the majority
of hockey players are male.

Happy conditioning.

PART I

The Conditioning Story

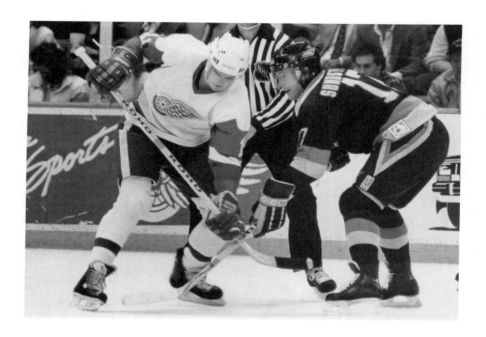

CHAPTER 1

What Can Be Conditioned?

Hockey is a multifaceted sport. For that reason, no single component of conditioning will provide overall improvement in performance. All facets of conditioning must at least be considered.

There are two general aspects of the human body that can be conditioned to improve hockey performance. One aspect is the muscle structures themselves. The other is the means of supplying energy to those muscles.

Think of work on the muscle structures as the construction industry in the body. You can have muscles of poured concrete, like the floor of a rink, or you can improve the structure by adding steel reinforcing rods to the concrete so it doesn't crumble with heavy wear and tear. In the muscle, the reinforcements are in the form of proteins. Yet muscles must be resilient as well as strong and durable, like the boards around the rink. You don't want them to snap when hit. Some degree of flexibility must be incorporated into the structure. So conditioning the muscle structures involves manipulation of protein structures to make a muscle strong, durable, and resilient.

Work on the energy supply systems for hockey is quite different from developing the muscle structures. A hockey arena can run on electricity, gas, oil, or a combination of fuels to create the energy needed to run the machines that make the ice, the heat, and the popcorn. Your body also gives you a variety of ways of creating the energy needed to run the muscles.

ATP (adenosine triphosphate) is the ultimate fuel used by the muscles. It is generated by breaking down fats, carbohydrates, and proteins. Conditioning the energy supply systems involves manipulation of these fuels and related chemicals to improve their supply and utilization.

In summary, there are six components of conditioning that can be used to improve a hockey player's performance. Three components affect muscle structures. They are strength, muscle endurance, and flexibility training. Three components affect energy supplies. They are anaerobic alactic, anaerobic lactic, and aerobic training.

Muscle Structures

Strength training, muscle endurance training, and flexibility work each affect a muscle's structure in different ways. A coach or player must be able to identify what it is he really wants to improve so that the most effective type of training is selected.

Strength Training

Strength training is associated with an increase in protein contractile units within the muscle. It's like putting eight sets of oars in a boat instead of four. With more protein (oars), more power can be generated. Protein tissue, which packages the muscle fibers, is also reinforced by strength training, which is an effect similar to switching from a cheap fabric equipment bag to a strong canvas one. The result of these increases in protein structures is that more force can be exerted and withstood by the muscle: The muscle becomes stronger.

Muscle Endurance Training

Muscle endurance training is associated with an increase in the size and number of energy-producing machines in the muscle cells. The machines, called mitochondria, are made of protein. Increasing the number of mitochondria is like increasing the number of scouts a team has. More scouts can watch more players, and even if one scout gets snowed in, another can fill in to get the job done. In the muscle, more and bigger mitochondria means there are more energy-generating stations available, so more work can be done at one time and if one station burns out, others can take over to get more work done. The muscle becomes more durable.

Flexibility Training

Flexibility training involves two functions in a muscle: the ability to stretch and the ability to recoil. Think of flexibility as being synonymous with elasticity. Most of the stretch of a muscle occurs toward the tendonous ends of a muscle, where muscle fibers are fewer and where the protein tissue which packages the muscle cells converges and forms a tendon. The tendency to recoil is more general across the muscle. Elasticity, allowing a muscle both to elongate fully and to snap back to its natural length, provides stability in the joint the muscle serves while allowing the joint to move through a large range of motion. This provides reduced risk of injury and the opportunity for greater power production.

Note that both stretch and recoil must be involved in training. If a muscle can only stretch, the joint is left loose and susceptible to injury. Conversely, the muscle that retains only tension has little distance over which power can be generated. Tight muscles are often associated with an imbalance in pull around a joint, which makes the joint prone to injury. Elasticity in a muscle makes it more resilient.

Energy Supply Systems

Anaerobic alactic, anaerobic lactic, and aerobic conditioning each contribute to the generation of ATP in different ways. The systems may all function to varying degrees at the same time; however, to train each effectively, a coach must be able to differentiate between them.

Anaerobic Alactic Training

Think of anaerobic alactic energy as explosive energy, the type used to snap the wrists on a shot or to take off to catch someone heading for a breakaway. Alactic energy is where quickness comes from in a player.

ATP, the chemical needed by muscles for movement, is stored right in the muscle cells, so it is available to fire up as soon as it is needed. Another chemical, PC (phosphocreatine), is also stored in the muscle cells. PC is used to regenerate ATP as soon as it fires.

These two stored chemicals allow a muscle to move very quickly, but only for a short time. The problem is that the gas tank is very small. The stored fuel runs out quickly. Then PC and consequently ATP must be regenerated from another fuel source. That is the end of explosive energy.

Even though traces of stored ATP and PC are still in the muscle up to 40 seconds after stimulation, peak power output by these chemicals seems to occur around 10 seconds. After that, you begin to "sputter" because the stored fuel level is dropping.

The stores of ATP and PC refill quickly, though, when the muscle gets a chance to rest. Most of the fuel can be replaced in about 60· seconds. So the anaerobic alactic system can be used over and over again as long as rest periods occur. In hockey, this happens frequently when the whistle blows for a face-off or a player gets to sit on the bench at the end of his shift.

Anaerobic alactic training results in bigger stores of ATP and PC so a player has more fuel to explode within the first 10 seconds. For hockey, that means quicker take-offs, more snappy wrist shots, and better maneuverability. Muscle contractions become quicker.

Anaerobic Lactic Training

Think of anaerobic lactic energy as the energy used for sustained speed. This is different from the explosive energy of the alactic system. The difference is seen if you try to run a 50-meter sprint as hard as you can possibly go. Then run a 500-meter sprint, again as fast as you can possibly go. You would find that each 50 meters of the 500-meter sprint is slower than the 50-meter sprint run by itself. That is because the alactic system cannot last as long as it takes to run 500 meters, so the muscles have to look elsewhere for ATP. When high speed is required for longer than 10 seconds, as in the 500-meter run, the lactic system is called on for energy. It produces reasonably high-powered energy, not as high as the alactic system but sustaining the energy production longer.

This high-powered, sustained energy is fueled by carbohydrates (CHO) that are stored in the muscles. There are also CHO stores in the blood and the liver that can be carried to the muscles as a back-up supply. But getting and using that fuel takes time, thus energy wanes. A well-trained anaerobic lactic system can provide high energy for up to 3 minutes, but it usually peaks between 40 and 90 seconds. Part of the reason for a time limit on this system is the drain in muscle CHO stores. Another factor is that the burning of CHO results in production of a waste product called lactic acid (LA). When LA levels get high in a muscle, chemical reactions are inhibited and the energy supply system cannot provide as high an output. Muscle action slows down.

When a muscle gets rest, it takes up to an hour to get rid of most of the LA, but it can take 48 hours or more to refill emptied muscle CHO stores (called glycogen). Active rest, such as easy skating or walking, helps get rid of LA more quickly. CHO must be eaten to refill glycogen stores quickly.

Anaerobic lactic training provides three advantages: greater stores of glycogen in the muscle, slower accumulation of LA, and greater tolerance to LA levels. For the hockey player, that means he can generate more speed and last longer at high speeds. In other words, he can go faster and keep it up for a whole 1-minute shift, instead of having his speed drop off after 30 seconds or so when there are no whistles. It also means that while he is sitting on the bench between shifts, he will have less LA to get rid of before his next shift. If less LA accumulates as the game goes on, he is less likely to lose his speed by the end of periods and games when he might need it most. Anaerobic lactic training gives a player a faster, more intense game.

Aerobic Training

Aerobic energy is what most people think of as endurance. The aerobic system includes the heart, lungs, and circulatory network as well as some very specific muscle chemistry. These things work together to provide ongoing energy to sleep, walk, or get through a practice. The aerobic system provides very constant energy because fat is the primary fuel for regenerating ATP. The supply of fat in the body is not likely to run out, so there is no time limit on this system. On the other hand, the intensity of energy is considerably less than either of the other two systems because the process of getting ATP from fat is very complex, and the fuel must be transported to the muscle before it can be used.

The aerobic energy supply system can also use CHO and protein as fuel for ATP regeneration. CHO is used when the upper limits of aerobic energy production are required, as when a player double-shifts for 10 to 12 minutes of a period. The LA system cannot last that long, yet high-intensity energy is required. So the aerobic system burns CHO because it produces energy more quickly than fat. Fat utilization doesn't stop; it is simply supplemented by CHO burning.

The aerobic system prefers not to use protein as an energy fuel because the body needs it for construction materials, as we have already seen. However, if fats and CHO are in low supply, as may be the case in a very lean player who has not eaten properly over two tournament days, some protein may be used to generate energy. This is not a desirable situation because acids are produced (keto acids) and valuable protein may be lost to the muscles. The player may finish the event, but intensity is inhibited.

The aerobic system serves a very important function beyond providing constant energy. It is the body's waste-removal and energy-replacement system. Aerobic energy allows the muscles to recover from the side effects of exercise, such as accumulated LA, empty muscle glycogen stores, and low ATP and PC levels.

A good aerobic system is crucial for a hockey player. Aerobic training provides a stronger, more efficient heart, better air exchange in the lungs, more effective transportation of goods (oxygen, fats, and CHO), and removal of wastes (LA and carbon dioxide) by the blood. This allows muscles to do their job more effectively. The muscles have to work at high speed during play, so the two anaerobic systems are needed for action. But the muscles get frequent rest, both during whistle stops and when the player sits on the bench between shifts. A good aerobic system allows a player to take advantage of these rests so that his muscles recover more completely. Then when he requires quickness and speed during the next shift, his muscles are fresh and ready to go.

The aerobic system provides the energy that gets a player through the 2 hours or so it takes to play a game. And it is the aerobic system that gets a player through hours of practice so that he can work hard enough to improve his skills, quickness, and speed. Aerobic training lets a player use his skills and speed to their maximum throughout the game.

Summary

A hockey player can influence his muscle structures and his energy supply systems by conditioning. The muscle structures will develop more contractile and connective protein, more protein-energy-producing machinery (mitochondria), and more elastic properties throughout the protein packages of the muscle. These changes come about as a result of strength, muscle endurance, and flexibility training respectively. The results are stronger, more durable, and more resilient muscles for use in the game. The energy supply systems improve fuel stores, the ability to utilize fuels, and the ability to recover from exercise as a result of anaerobic alactic, anaerobic lactic, and aerobic training. This allows players to improve their quickness, speed, endurance, and ability to recover so they can use their skills at peak levels through every minute of every game.

CHAPTER 2

What Is Inherent to Conditioning?

Each type of conditioning listed in chapter 1 has a very specific set of principles that must be followed to ensure that you get the appropriate physical and chemical changes to occur in the muscles and energy supplies. Before you consider these specific training principles, there are some underlying conditions that should be understood regardless of which type of training you are working on. These conditions apply regardless of the age, skill level, or fitness level of the players. They can be used in setting training objectives for players and to optimize the effect of training on players.

Overload and Adaptation

The muscles and energy supply systems of the body are very adaptable. They improve easily if they are given the need and encouragement to do so. That need is created by overloading the component you want to improve just enough that the body can handle it with some effort, like lifting a slightly heavier weight when you want to improve strength. When the heavier weight is used repeatedly, the muscle gets used to handling the extra load, and that capability becomes the new ''normal'' level. If you want further improvement, you then have to set a new overload.

This is the technique behind proper conditioning of any type. Assign a slight overload, then give time for the body to adapt to it. Repeat this procedure until you attain the level of fitness you require to perform the sport appropriately. This technique applies to training strength, endurance, flexibility, and the energy supply systems.

There are two keys to using the technique effectively. One is that improvement comes most quickly when the overloads are small. Too big an overload will delay adaptation and can cause both physical injury, which can set a player back by weeks, and the psychological stress of not being able to get beyond a certain level.

The second key to effective adaptation is that sufficient time must be allowed for adaptation to occur. There is no precise time in days or hours, but the coach or player must judge when a particular workload becomes comfortable to handle, such as when he can do the last two repeats almost as easily as the first two. Then it is time to increase the load.

For example, if a 14-year-old were given sit-ups to do as a muscle endurance exercise, he may start with three sets of 15 sit-ups per set. If he walked away from that regime saying "No sweat," you might up the load to 20 repeats each set the next training day. However, if the last few sit-ups of each set were performed with difficulty, you should leave him at three sets of 15 until he can complete them with minimal slowdown. Then increase the load by two each set until, over the course of a few weeks, he gets to his target of 25 or 30 sit-ups per set. Increase the load only when the prescribed regime can be handled. It should take effort, but not involve great difficulty.

The keys to effective training of any kind are to overload little by little and to allow time for adaptation between each overload.

Reversibility

The opposite of overload and adaptation is reversibility, which means that anything that can be conditioned can also be undone by lack of use. For example, a hockey player who gets the flu and is laid up for 5 days will lose some of his conditioning. The rule of thumb is that losses will be at approximately the same rate as were the gains. In other words, if this player gets the flu just when he finishes a week of training camp and that was all the conditioning he had bothered to do in preparation for the season, he would be back where he started in conditioning when he returned to play following the illness.

Reversibility is why it is so important for hockey players to consider conditioning to be a way of life, just like eating and sleeping. Conditioning that is developed steadily over the years is not quickly lost. When playoffs roll around and there is no time for practice or conditioning, the player who has worked out regularly will suffer only minimal losses in conditioning. Whether he is struck by sickness, injury, or lack of practice time, the player who has made conditioning a regular part of life will not be set back as far as will a player who did a crash course to get in shape. Players must be conscious of reversibility of conditioning and combat it by taking an ongoing, steady approach to training.

Specificity

Specificity refers to the fact that aspects of conditioning improve only when a specific aspect is stimulated to adapt. There are two important implications of this principle for hockey. The first refers to the type of training you are trying to do. Specificity of training means that strength training, for example, will not automatically improve quickness; strength and quickness are two different things. Strength is a structural change in the protein of the muscle, and speed is a chemical change in an energy supply network. Specificity means that, by doing strength training, only the protein structures of the muscle are stimulated to improve. If you want some quickness developed in that muscle as well, you have to do some quickness training, something that overloads the anaerobic alactic energy supply system.

This is not to say that two or more elements cannot be trained at once. They can, but the training must be designed carefully to include each element's specific set of training principles. Using the same example, if a player wished to train quickness at the same time as he worked to improve his strength, he would have to push a heavy weight (for strength) very fast (for quickness). Note that some training combinations, such as this one, are difficult to perform and should only be done using very safe equipment and conditions, such as having a spotter when using free weights.

Recognize that when you use combination exercises, each fitness element's improvement is compromised to some extent. In other words, neither element will improve as quickly as when trained by itself. That is not necessarily negative. An athlete may not need peak levels of that element quickly. The advantages and disadvantages of various combinations of training must be weighed and selected according to what suits the player's needs. For example, it may be that a team only gets one practice a week. In this case, the time-saving advantage of combination training far outweighs the slight reduction in the speed of improvement.

Another example is a 12-year-old who needs more strength. Pure strength training is not advised for a fast-growing 12-year-old. It is much safer to do combination strength/endurance work, such as working up to 25 regular push-ups, then switching to work up to 25 feet-elevated push-ups. This combination will still provide strength improvements, but to a lesser degree than would a pure strength exercise because specificity is being compromised. Conversely, a professional player who has lost some strength due to a layoff would not want to compromise on getting his strength back quickly. He would do best to get access to a Cybex® type of machine and work at peak strength levels with far fewer repeats.

The principle of specificity also applies to training specifically for on-ice hockey. Hockey requires certain muscles to be used through unique ranges of motion at particular speeds. This means that very specific chemicals and nerve pathways are used. Those exact muscles, nerves, and chemicals must be stimulated to adapt precisely for the demands of performance in a game. In a practical sense, this means that generalized conditioning is useful to establish a sound base early in the season or preferably in the off-season. But by the time games become important, training must be very specific to the actions involved in hockey. For example, running is a good way of doing aerobic and anaerobic conditioning. But running uses leg muscles differently from how skating uses them. So although running can be used in the off-season or to maintain a general base in conditioning during the season, ultimately, in season, some very specific aerobic and anaerobic training drills should be conducted on ice using skating.

Similarly, hockey players are often tempted to use the weight training programs of body builders. They look good. But hockey players need muscle structures very different from those needed by body builders, weight lifters, or shot putters. So players must use programs designed specifically for hockey.

In summary, specificity applies to conditioning for hockey in two ways. Players should train according to the specific principles for each component of conditioning they want to develop, and they should train precise muscles, nerves, and chemicals in the specific manner they will be used in a game. There is a time and place for combination training. But ultimately, precise muscles, angles, speed, frequency of use, rest periods, exercise time, and intensity should be simulated.

Heredity and Individual Differences

''He's a natural athlete.'' You have heard that statement before. There is some truth to the adage that athletes are born, not made. But the matter is less crucial to hockey than to some other sports. This is because hockey requires such a broad range of abilities that it is unlikely for anyone to have been born with all of them. For example, a smaller player can excel at the game as a forward if he maximizes speed and quickness along with his skills. Conversely, a huge, bulky player with less speed may also excel at the game, but probably as a defenseman if he optimizes his play-reading and checking skills.

People are born with different muscle content and different potential in body structure. However, the important thing for hockey is to recognize that all aspects of fitness can be improved by conditioning whether a player be large or small, male or female. A player who has less genetic potential in, for example, cardiovascular (aerobic) fitness can still develop so that fatigue does not influence his game any more than someone who was born with more aerobic structures.

Conditioning can make a difference. Genetics merely sets the upper limits. And in hockey, the upper limits are not as critical as they are, for example, in marathon running or in high jumping.

The other side of the heredity issue is that people do not all develop their genetic potential at the same rate. You are familiar with the 12-year-old girl who is taller than all the players on your 12-year-old boys' team. Or you remember the boy who was the smallest kid on the team at 12 years old. When you saw him at

18 years old, he was 190 centimeters (6 foot, 3 inches) tall and weighed 94 kilograms (207 pounds). That is a nice size for a defenseman, so one would hope he hadn't been discouraged from playing hockey due to his size when he was 12.

A normal growth pattern is that the person who grows up earliest peaks soonest, and the slower growers usually go right on to end up taller at maturity. So don't throw a small player out too quickly. Parents cannot always be used as a guide to the size of a player because genes frequently skip a generation. So small parents can have a 6-foot son, if the grandparents had some height.

The concept of varying rates of development is also true for conditioning. This means that a single team training program will not elicit the same rate of improvement in all players. For some players, the program may involve excessive overload, slowing their improvement, while for others it may be perfect for quick improvement. The ideal would be to have individual programs for all players; but you would need to hire a fitness consultant to monitor all the programs, so it is impractical in most cases. The next best thing is simply for a coach to recognize that each player will differ in his needs and his responses to a conditioning program and to allow for individual differences when setting goals and expectations. Not every player should be expected to run 5-minute miles after a 6-week aerobic conditioning program. But everyone can improve their mile pace.

In summary, heredity can provide some advantages and disadvantages for hockey players. It will influence how quickly and to what extent a player's body grows and adapts to conditioning challenges. But more important is the fact that conditioning can be used to minimize inherited disadvantages and to maximize inherited bonuses so that a wide variety of heredity packages can play an excellent game of hockey. Coaches must recognize that individual variation will come out in a team, particularly during the growing years. The variance can be accommodated by setting a range of goals and expectations.

The Age Factor

Age must be considered when planning training programs. However, it is not the years, but the growth that is the concern during youth. In other words, it is not accurate to say that at 14 years old, a player should not do heavy weight training, but at 18, he can do all he wants. Growth, not age, should be the determining factor.

A useful habit is for coaches or players to keep a monthly growth chart. During periods of rapid growth, heavy strength training and hard anaerobic lactic training are contraindicated. Both these types of training are hard on the joints, which is where most growth takes place. They also involve considerable wear and tear on muscle tissue and chemical balances. The growing body already has plenty of construction and balancing to do to handle the stress of growth, so there is frequently little energy left for hard training. Time spent on strength or lactic training may be wasted and may even be dangerous while the body is growing rapidly.

Another consideration of the age factor is at the other end of the age spectrum, the old timers. People 35 years and up are capable of doing any type of training and they can improve any aspect of fitness with training. But there are a couple of things to keep in mind. First is to be realistic about your beginning fitness level. Don't assume you can do the same things you did when you quit playing hockey 15 or so years ago. Start training at an easy level and proceed gradually. That is the quickest way to good condition and minimal risk of injury.

Second, anaerobic lactic training is very stressful on the heart. An old timer should develop a good aerobic base before attempting any amount of LA training. Aerobic training is the best way of strengthening the heart and clearing the blood vessels so that there is minimal risk of aggravating a cardiovascular disorder. An old timer should get a complete physical, and preferably a stress test, from a doctor before starting a training program.

Third, old timers must include flexibility training in their program. Strain-type injuries (e.g., pulled muscles) are much too common in old timers' hockey. Flexibility training can return some of the elasticity lost around joints due to inactivity.

Age should be considered in planning training programs when growth is occurring at a rapid rate and when old timers decide to return to active duty. All ages can train all aspects of fitness and expect improvement. But fast-growing youths and old timers must be more selective and more conscientious about what they are doing and how it is affecting them.

Summary

Regardless of what a coach or player wishes to condition, factors like overload and adaptation, reversibility, specificity, heredity, individual differences, and age must be accommodated if optimal conditioning results are to be obtained. Training objectives and expectations should reflect these factors so that both the physiological and psychological development of the player progresses as planned.

CHAPTER 3

What Inhibits Conditioning?

A coach can provide the best conditioning program known to hockey, yet on-ice performance may not reflect the quality of the program at all. A variety of things can compromise the efforts of players, coaches, or the grand design. Some can be controlled to a large extent, but for others you can only prepare as best you can to minimize their influence on performance.

Nutrition for Hockey Players

Poor nutrition will inhibit performance. Conversely, good nutrition will allow an athlete to make the most of his ability. But what is good nutrition? There are probably more myths and fads about what athletes should and should not eat than about any other single aspect of performance. For example, claims that protein supplements give you stronger muscles, that vitamin E gives you more energy, or that athletic drinks are for everybody, can be misleading. They make the area of nutrition for athletes seem confusing. There is a simpler side.

Basic Needs

Foods are made up of various combinations of CHO, fat, protein, vitamins, minerals, and water. All of these elements are needed by athletes. The CHOs and fats provide most of the fuel for energy to play the game. Fats also are important for vitamin storage, for shock absorption around internal organs, and for assistance in temperature regulation. Proteins and some minerals, such as calcium and sodium, are used in construction and function of muscles, bones, and nerve and blood pathways. Vitamins and other minerals are crucial elements in the chemical processes that allow action to occur. For example, iron is a mineral in the blood that transports oxygen for the aerobic system.

Water is the medium in which all chemical reactions occur. If water is limited, chemical reactions are inhibited and performance is stifled. Too little water can even lead to death, as has occurred with a number of football players and distance runners. Water provides the cooling mechanism for the body machinery and facilitates waste removal. Both of these functions are important during exercise. An athlete should eat a wide variety of foods and drink plenty of water (2 1/2 liters per day, including what comes in foods, as in apples).

Quantity

Good nutrition can be achieved by eating 2 to 4 servings of milk products daily, 2 servings of meat products, 3 to 5 servings of grain products, and 4 to 5 servings of fruits and vegetables each day. One serving is usually 125 milliliters (1/2 cup). Milk products, however, use 250 milliliters (1 cup), and one serving of meat or cheese is 60 to 90 grams (2 to 3 ounces).

This combination of eating will provide the nutrition a body needs, assuming that foods used are fresh and have undergone minimal processing which destroys some of the nutrients. This combination of servings provides 4,000 to 6,000 kilojoules (1,000 to 1,400 kilocalories) per day, which is sufficient to maintain the weight of a sedentary person. A hockey player obviously needs more calories than that. It takes 40 to 50 kilojoules (10 to 12 kilocalories) per minute to provide the energy needed for strong skating (not bench sitting). It is common for a hockey player to need an additional 12,000 to 16,000 kilojoules (3,000 to 4,000 kilocalories) per day above that provided by minimal nutrition food quantities to fulfill the energy requirements of practices, games, and daily activity. These additional caloric needs are best met by increasing the servings in the grains and fruit and vegetable food groups. These are high in CHO, which is the major fuel used in the game.

Additional protein is not usually required by hockey players. They tend to eat more protein than the minimum serving requires, as a normal eating habit. Most of the extra protein is simply released in the urine. Some protein may be converted to fat for fuel.

A player needs to eat the required servings from the four food groups to cover basic nutrition. Then he should get the additional calories he needs from grains and fruits and vegetables.

Supplements

The adage that "more is better" does not seem to hold true for athletes. Once the body has adequate amounts of what it needs, it seems to make no further use of extras. It gets rid of many of them, such as extra protein and many vitamins. Others are more difficult to eliminate and may cause problems, such as vitamin toxicity. So, good nutrition is worthy of attention, but time and money spent on major supplementation is often wasted.

The exception is the player who is at risk of malnutrition. This might be a player who does not eat regular meals, who eats few fruits and vegetables, or who eats more processed foods than fresh. If a player does not eat a well-balanced diet, a multivitamin and mineral supplement that contains no more than the Recommended Dietary Allowance (RDA) is advisable because performance can be adversely affected. (See Table 3.1 for a list of RDAs.) Megadoses are expensive and do not provide any performance benefits beyond what good basic nutrition provides.

Frequency

Eating times for a hockey player are often erratic. Practices are scheduled at dinner time; early games interfere with breakfast; tournaments don't allow a good chance to eat. The important thing is to eat a good breakfast every day and after that, eat at least two more times that day. A player does not have to have three sit-down meals a day. It can be just as healthy to eat up to five more times over the course of the day if schedules interfere with normal eating times. The total number of calories taken in should not change. Use the same servings and food groups listed above. Frequent eating is advisable for individuals who have large appetites or wide swings in blood sugar levels (such as diabetics). It is a healthy habit that is easy to adjust to erratic schedules.

Table 3.1 Recommended Dietary Allowance (RDA) of Vitamins and Minerals

	RDA[a]
Vitamins	
A	5,000 IU
B-6	2 mg
B-12	6 mcg
C	60 mg
D	400 IU
E	30 IU
Folic acid	400 mcg
Niacin	20 mg
Pantothenic acid	10 mg
Riboflavin	2 mg
Thiamine	1.5 mg
Minerals	
Copper	2 mg
Iodine	150 mcg
Iron	18 mg
Zinc	15 mg
Manganese[b]	—
Potassium[b]	—
Selenium[b]	—

Note. RDAs are recommended minimums for generally healthy adults. Growth, stress, smoking, drinking, and poor eating habits can render these minimums insufficient. Under these conditions, you would be well advised to adjust your intake accordingly, on the advice of a nutritionist.

[a]mcg, microgram; mg, milligram; IU, International Units.

[b]Recognized as essential, but no RDA established.

Special Situations

Even players who have nutritionally sound diets encounter situations in which they need to manipulate eating habits temporarily. A player may report to training camp overweight. Another player may need to put on some weight. A whole team may have to eat at unusual times and in varying amounts because of tournaments or back-to-back games. Adjustments can usually be made with ease if you remember a few key points.

Weight Reduction. A hockey player is not usually advised to go on a severely restricted diet, even if he is overweight, particularly during the season. A severe reduction in calories is likely to result in a lack of energy for practices and games. However, if a player is carrying too much fat weight (which should be determined by body composition assessment, not weight scales and tables of population norms), weight can be reduced without interfering with performance. To lose fat weight, a player should first cut out the "empty calorie" foods, such as commercial snack foods, sugared soft drinks, and desserts. Second, he should limit intake of meat and dairy products to the minimum servings indicated above. Third, he should take a daily 20- to 30-minute exercise session, such as an easy jog, brisk walk, or comfortable bike ride, at some part of the day apart from practice or game times. First thing in the morning is often most workable. A weight loss of up to 1 kilogram (2 pounds) per week is ideal. Weight that is lost any faster tends to return just as quickly, and the dieter does not have sufficient energy for practices and games. Practices and games should continue as usual for the players who are working at weight reduction.

Adding Weight. It is easy to add fat weight, as most people know. But that is not the kind of weight that helps a player on the ice. If a hockey player needs more weight for his position, it is best to put on muscle weight. The weight is then functional instead of excess baggage. Strength and explosive power training are the best ways to increase functional weight. An increase of up to 2 kilograms (4 pounds) per week can occur initially. Protein supplements are not usually necessary as long as the recommended servings of protein foods are eaten. If training is particularly intense, though, slightly larger servings of protein foods (meat, cheese, milk products) ensure sufficient protein availability.

Putting weight on young players is a questionable practice. Because their growing bodies should not be subjected to heavy strength training programs, a combination strength/endurance program using primarily body weight as resistance can be effective. The young player's functional weight will increase, though at a slower and safer rate than would occur with a pure strength training program.

Pregame Eating.   There are three times when intake of food is important preceding game time. The first is the 24-hour period before the game or tournament. This is the last chance a player has to ensure that he has adequate nutrition to fulfill the requirements of game performance. This is the time to make sure all fuel stores are topped up rather than being left partially depleted due to heavy practices the days before. It is also time to set the body up so that dehydration will not become a problem. Plenty of carbohydrates (pastas, rice, breads, fruit desserts) should be eaten during this period to top up glycogen stores. Food should include some salt, so electrolyte balance is restored, and plenty of water should be ingested. Any practice should be light, to eliminate the risk of having only partially replenished fuel, electrolyte, and water stores by game time.

The second time to be conscious of pregame eating is 3 to 4 hours before game time. The concern at this point is prevention—how to keep hunger at bay for the next few hours without causing any side effects from eating. It is virtually too late to expect the foods you eat at this time to contribute in a significant way to fuel supplies. They take too long to be processed (fats up to 10 hours, proteins up to 14 hours, CHO up to 6 hours). A light, predominately CHO meal should be eaten at least 3 hours prior to game time. Some protein can be included in this meal (e.g., tuna in a salad or sandwich) because protein stays longer in the stomach, warding off a feeling of hunger. Fluids should also be included in the meal to top up water supplies.

The timing is important because you want most food to have left the stomach by game time so you are not feeling heavy and full at game time. Most CHO clears the stomach within 3 hours. Having food in the stomach attracts blood flow to the area. This is not desirable when the muscles need the blood for supply and cleanup.

The third time to consider ingestion is during the last hour before game time. During this period, only water should be taken. Anything containing salts or sugars could interfere with performance because salt and sugar sit in the stomach and restrict the amount of fluid that is free to be used in the body. This can lead to early dehydration problems. Also, as sugars get into the blood, they cause an insulin response that can leave the blood depleted of CHO just about game time. Both muscles and the brain need that blood sugar when the game begins. Many players who have not heeded this advice have noticed a sluggish feeling when they step onto the ice. The mind is willing but the legs are weak. So players should avoid sugared drinks and chocolate bars within 1 hour of game or practice time. Drink water only.

Some elite teams have begun the practice of having coffee available in the dressing room before games or practices. Coffee has two effects that may influence performance. The caffeine in coffee stimulates the nervous system and exerts a glycogen-sparing effect in the muscles. These effects can occur as a result of ingestion of as little as half a cup of strong black coffee. The caffeine in tea and chocolate can exert similar effects, but it takes greater amounts, which may result in a blood shunt to the stomach. Chocolate is not advisable due to the insulin response it creates.

The use of coffee as an aid to performance has been questioned as an ethical issue. Caffeine is classed as an ergogenic aid, like amphetamines and steroids. But because coffee is ingested as a normal daily habit by many older hockey players, it is difficult to ban it as an artificial aid to performance. Perhaps the bigger question regarding its use is whether or not it is actually useful for hockey players.

Certainly there is some advantage to having the nerves stimulated so that messages are transmitted more quickly. Hockey is a game of speed and reaction time. But caffeine can also overstimulate the nerves, making a person jittery and his movements more spastic. This would detract from hockey performance. These effects are common in young players and inexperienced coffee drinkers. So if coffee is going to be ingested, it should be done at practices so that an individual can check its effects. Even at that, there may be some surprises. Higher stress levels, such as are encountered at game time, can have the nerves already stimulated, and the coffee that was good for practice can suddenly be too much. Young players' responses to caffeine are frequently erratic, so they should probably not be encouraged to ingest coffee; normal motivation should be sufficient to stimulate their nerves. Also, caffeine is thought to have some addictive properties, so its initial effectiveness may decrease as time goes on.

The glycogen-sparing effect provided by coffee ingestion is probably only of use for players who play 10 minutes of every period, for teams that go into long overtimes, and for teams playing two or three games on consecutive days. It takes 2 hours or more of fairly intense activity to deplete glycogen stores. With all the bench-sitting most hockey players do, glycogen stores are usually sufficient to handle a game and do not need to be spared.

Ingestion During the Game or Practice.   Water is a must during games and practices. Ideally, each player should have his own bottle; this provides less risk of spreading communicable diseases, in addition to providing an opportunity to monitor water intake. Coaches are advised to have players take in up to 125 milliliters (two or three good swallows) every 15 minutes. This prevents the onset of dehydration and yet the amount is small enough that the stomach never gets a full feeling or sufficient content to require a shunting of blood to the stomach area. Commercial athletic drinks are not advisable for hockey players during the game. The main reason is that they are unnecessary; sugar and electrolyte levels are unlikely to run into shortages during the game if the player has eaten according to earlier recommendations. Second, if a player does any amount of bench-sitting during the game, athletic drinks could cause insulin response problems so that when he does step on the ice, his blood sugar levels are too low. A third point is that many commercial solutions sit in the stomach, which may result in water being diverted from the blood to the stomach to dilute the solution, and the solution may stay too long in the stomach to be useful during the game anyway. One exception to this general rule of water only during a practice or game is when players are subjected to more than one game a day during tournament play. In this case, a dilute commercial preparation may be used to help maintain CHO levels. It should be ingested in the same small amounts as water, more than 1 hour before game time, immediately after the game, and possibly during actual playing time. Those who get little ice time should still ingest water only during the game.

Eating After the Game or Practice.   A player who gets plenty of ice time and who plays most of the game at high intensity will use up much of his CHO stores by the end of a game. His water balance may also be lowered. The best way to get back to normal quickly is to eat a high carbohydrate snack or meal and drink plenty of fluids after the game. This is particularly important when the team must play again the next day. It takes up to 48 hours to replace emptied CHO stores when CHO is eaten in large amounts. If CHOs are not ingested to any degree, it can take up to 5 days to replace muscle stores. A player cannot afford to go into a subsequent game short of CHO.

Many older players are in the habit of having beer after a game. It is true that beer is high in CHO, water, and some minerals and electrolytes. But the alcohol in beer is also a diuretic, which means that more water will be lost in the urine than if you did not have that beer. Along with that water go a number of nutrients, such as B vitamins, calcium, and magnesium, that are necessary for good performance. The result is that you lose some of what you most need to replace by consuming alcohol after a game. This is particularly important if you have a game the next day.

The best system is not to drink alcohol within 24 hours of a game. Other nights, when you have beer after a game, realize that one or two beers is not sufficient to significantly interfere with nutrition in a nutritionally balanced adult. But you should get into the habit of drinking one or two large glasses of water before and after having the beer to minimize the beer's effect on water replacement. On those rare occasions when you consume more than a couple of beers, make an effort to drink large amounts of water throughout the evening as you drink the beer. You may also be well advised to take a vitamin supplement the next day.

There are many reasons for eliminating alcohol within 24 hours of a game. Alcohol hurts performance by interfering with power generation, reaction time, coordination, and cardiovascular efficiency, which may result in poor temperature regulation, energy production, and recovery. It can take up to 48 hours to regain normal function in all these factors. Athletes must drink responsibly if they are going to drink.

Nutrition for hockey players is based on eating a variety of foods in particular proportions from four specific food groups. They must also drink plenty of fluids. Extra calories are needed to supply the energy for practices and games. These should come mostly from the high CHO food groups, grains and fruits and vegetables. As game time approaches, manipulation of CHO and water are the priorities.

Overtraining

There is such a thing as too much of a good thing. Training can be overdone. The symptoms are lethargy in performance, occurrence of stress-type injuries, or staleness in improvement. The cause is usually too large an overload or insufficient rest. The importance of reasonable overload was discussed in chapter 2.

Many players and coaches do not recognize the importance of rest. One very specific requirement of a training session is the rest interval. Without rest intervals, improvement is hampered. This means that days of rest are also important. The body needs time to adjust to training stimuli. If it works hard every day, there is no time to adjust completely. So the body falls behind in its attempts to keep up with adaptations.

One day off per week is the minimum recommended. With fast-growing youths, every 3rd day off is more reasonable. However, it should be noted that rest does not necessarily mean doing nothing. The old adage that a change is as good as a rest is valid. For instance, a mild, flowing workout that is done at a completely different pace from the usual high intensity sessions, such as an hour bike hike or orienteering outing, can be refreshing for the body and the mind. But if workouts, game schedules, and pressure have been consistently demanding for some time, a day off will do more good than harm. Rest can be effective mentally as well as physically.

Overtraining often occurs when players get very enthusiastic about conditioning. They tend to try to take bigger adjustments than their body can quickly handle, or they take too few breaks to allow time for the body to adjust. Small, frequent overload and regular passive rest or a change of pace (to something easy and flowing) can minimize the risk of suffering from overtraining.

Environment

Few players practice in outdoor rinks where cold and windchill factors are an environmental concern. Quite the contrary, many players practice in heated rinks or play to large crowds that heat up the environment. In addition, hockey equipment can act to conserve body heat. So a more common environmental concern for players today is overheating. The danger of overheating is that it can lead to dehydration, which impairs performance.

There are a number of things a player can do to minimize the negative effects of overheating on performance. One is to anticipate when this is likely to occur. You may be going to play in a hot rink, or playoffs may be stretching into an unusually warm spring. In these cases, practice in the heat if possible (while you drink lots of water) and drink an excess of water in the 24-hour period preceding game time. This will have the body's cooling stores topped up to handle the heat.

Sweating is fine as long as the body has a good supply of water available and as long as the sweat can be evaporated. So the second thing to do is to drink water frequently (up to 125 ml per 15 minutes) during exposure to the heat. Do not use a commercial preparation in these conditions; it slows absorption of water to the blood system at a time when your body needs water most.

The third thing to do is to wear clothing and equipment that allow for good air circulation. T-shirts and socks made of cotton or wool are better than synthetic fibers. Leather breathes better than plastics. When you must use synthetic or plastic equipment check that it is designed with ventilation in mind. There should be perforations or a mesh fabric where possible.

Neither practices nor games should be done in plastic or rubberized sweat suits. Such suits do not increase the amount of fat burned. You lose weight, but it is just water and will return with subsequent meals. These suits put a player at too much risk of suffering from overheating.

A hot environment can lead to impaired performance regardless of the condition you are in. To avoid problems, drink plenty of fluids in the 24-hour period leading up to heat exposure, drink small amounts of water frequently during exposure, and dress to facilitate air circulation.

Illness and Injury

All players run some risk of succumbing to disease or injury regardless of the condition they are in. Well-conditioned players tend to suffer fewer illnesses and injuries, and they usually recover more quickly from layoff. But illness and injury cannot be avoided entirely.

When illness or injury strikes, it is best to lay off completely at first. Trying to continue with practice or play simply prolongs recovery; if the illness is a communicable disease such as flu or throat infection, the problem could be spread to other team members. Resume practice on the advice of a doctor.

When a player returns from a layoff, conditioning should start at a level he finds very easy. On succeeding days, he can take overload at a quicker pace than the first time he began to retrain. It is important that the player not jump right back in where he left off, but that he remember he will have lost conditioning at approximately the same pace at which he first acquired it.

In the end, be sure that a player clearly returns to the level he was at initially. Incomplete retraining, which for the most part can be prevented, is one of the main reasons players suffer recurring injuries.

Any player can get sick or injured. A well-conditioned player generally has lower incidence of and quicker recovery from illness and injury. However, when problems strike, lay off completely; then, when appropriate, return to conditioning at an easy level and overload progressively until the player reaches his previous level.

Stress

Many players show signs of difficulty controlling stress. They get too uptight and their performance becomes less productive, or they have difficulty sleeping. There are a variety of ways a player can learn to control the negative side effects of stress. Conditioning itself is known to help many people. Physicians, psychotherapists, physiotherapists, and others provide other approaches to stress management. However, there is a technique that players can learn to use themselves when they run into problems. It is known as a progressive relaxation technique. Players must practice progressive relaxation to make it effective.

Players should be instructed according to the explanation provided in Figure 3.1.

The technique can take up to half an hour the first time. But with practice, the whole regime can be completed in 15 minutes. It is

Figure 3.1
The Progressive Relaxation Technique.

Step 1. Go to a room where there is complete silence and darkness (no external stimuli). Lie flat on your back (either on the floor or a hard mattress, no pillows). Concentrate first on overall relaxation. Feel as if your whole body is sinking heavily. Think of nothing but the heavy feeling you are experiencing. This may take 2 or 3 minutes.

Step 2. Tense, then relax, every part of the body, one part at a time. Begin with the feet. Curl the toes under and squeeze the muscles of the whole foot as tight as possible for a slow 6 count. Then release the tension very slowly, as if the tension is draining out, like the last honey being poured from a jar. The last feeling is one of the feet sinking into the floor. Stay with that relaxed, sinking feeling for at least 1 minute. Concentrate on the sinking feeling.

Steps 3 to 11. Repeat the tighten-hold-release-drain-sink sequence for successive areas of the body, working from the feet up. Concentrate on the lower leg muscles, then the upper leg, the buttocks, the stomach, the hands, the biceps, the chest/shoulder area, the neck, and finally the face. Think only of the body part and the feeling you are trying to get.

Step 12. When each area of your body has been done separately, tense your entire body as tight as possible for the 6 count, then release, drain, and sink heavily, totally relaxed.

an ideal way to drop off to sleep the night before or after a stressful game.

Once a player becomes adept at inducing the drained, relaxed feeling, the technique can be used in shortened form to spot-control mounting stress. For example, just before a critical playoff game, the top scorer, who may have been in a bit of a slump lately, may notice that he doesn't really loosen up with warm-up. When he goes back to the dressing room, or even sitting on the bench, he can use the relaxation technique on the areas of his body where he feels most tense, such as in the stomach or in the shoulders. He should tighten, release, and drain each area. If he is practiced at the technique, just a few key points and a couple of minutes can be all it takes to relax enough to play better.

Much of the stress a player encounters can be controlled by self-administration of a relaxation technique. If this technique is not effective, professional help may be advisable.

Attitude

The best conditioning program in the world will go to waste if players do not have a positive attitude toward training. Some players have never been involved in a good conditioning program so they do not know what to expect. Some coaches have never used a formal conditioning program and are not as sure of themselves as they would like to be. There are a number of things that can be done to cultivate a positive environment for conditioning.

Coaches should tell players the focus or theme of the practice. For example, it may be an anaerobic training practice in which you also want to work on puck skills and breakouts. Then illustrate or explain the practice plan in the dressing room before going onto the ice. When players know what to expect, they tend to work harder at it.

Be specific when describing a drill, regarding both the purpose of the drill and the details, such as how long, how hard, and in which directions. Confusion on the ice can lead to inattentiveness and impatience and will detract from the quality of effort.

Include a fun component in practices as much as possible, regardless of the age group. Use of minicompetitions is one way of setting a fun challenge. Set targets with the intent being how close a player can get, not failure if he does not reach it. Avoid using conditioning drills as punishment.

Use testing as a positive part of the conditioning program. Educate players about conditioning and get them involved in the ''how'' and ''why'' of testing. When they see improvement, there will be positive psychological spinoffs.

Budget your time carefully. Use a stopwatch rather than guessing. Check your sequence of drills, allowing for rest periods, water breaks, variety, and no waste of time between drills. Time and accuracy are two factors that players recognize, and they can be used to generate a positive atmosphere.

Do a seasonal plan. Include monthly and weekly breakdowns. This allows better practice planning and avoids gaps in training and practice sessions. It gives a coach time to get answers to anything he questions. This leaves a coach feeling prepared and confident about his practices.

Good planning, careful use of time, education, and a fun and positive approach on the part of the coach will help create a positive attitude within the team toward conditioning.

Summary

A player's level of conditioning and performance can be hampered by such things as poor nutrition and eating habits, overtraining, hot environments, illness and injury, uncontrolled stress, and negative attitude. However, each factor can be manipulated to allow the effects of conditioning to be maximized and to be reflected in the player's performance.

Hockey Conditioning Principles and Programs

CHAPTER 4

Training for Muscle Strength and Endurance

Muscle strength and endurance are basic building blocks of a hockey player's body. The better the quality, the better base his skills have to work from. Muscle strength and endurance determine how hard a player can perform individual skills and how often he can repeat them without tiring. Strength is a big factor in such skills as hard shots and strong strides. Muscle endurance is what lets a player repeat those movements at the same level of strength. The combination of strength and endurance is what helps a player hold a position and interfere with an opposing player's actions.

Even though muscle strength and endurance are quite different things in the muscle (strength comes from the protein structures within and around a muscle, while muscle endurance comes from the size and number of energy-producing machines within the muscle cells), it is obvious from hockey examples that strength and endurance are used in combination in most hockey actions.

Strength and endurance can be trained independently if either needs particular emphasis. However, because hockey uses them so much in combination, it is usually more practical to do combination training. Pure strength training is also rather hard on joints and muscles, so unless maximum strength is needed as quickly as possible, combination training is recommended as the more appropriate technique.

Specificity is a big factor in muscle strength and endurance training. Hockey uses many muscles and at a tremendous variety of angles and speeds. This makes it difficult to design a precise hockey strength training program. A good program includes an exercise for each of the major joint and muscle actions that can be simulated. The actual strength/endurance is developed first. Then the speed factor is carefully incorporated.

It is important to work with safe equipment when using weights for strength/endurance training. A spotter (an assistant who is ready to support the weight if the player exercising cannot) is necessary when working with free weights.

Neither strength nor endurance programs need to be done using expensive weight training equipment. Body weight, mechanical advantage, and cheap flexible tubing can all be used to manipulate resistance and specificity. The use of a partner is practical for providing resistance and for allowing reasonable rest intervals between work efforts.

The principles for separate training of strength and muscle endurance are presented below so that coaches can differentiate the training requirements. The principles for doing combination training are also presented, and it is recommended that these be used in training hockey players. Remember that fast growing youths should do only combination strength/endurance training.

Principles of Strength Training

Rapid improvement in strength will occur if all of the following requirements are met. But these should be pursued with caution, as this training creates high physical stress on circulation, muscles, and joints, and is rarely used as an optimal form of training for any athlete.

Resistance	•	maximum, near 100%
Repetitions	•	1 to 3
Sets	•	3
Frequency	•	once every 48 hours

Principles of Muscle Endurance Training

Muscle endurance training is comparatively easy on circulation, muscles, and joints. Improvements come with adherence to the following requirements.

Resistance • up to 50%
Repetitions • 20 to 30
Sets • 1 to 3
Frequency • 3 to 6 times per week

Principles of Combination Strength/Endurance Training

Hockey players need a combination of muscle strength and endurance, usually with slightly more emphasis on the strength portion. Effective combination programs fall within the ranges outlined below. Select resistance and repetitions toward the end of the range that is closest to the element you most want to develop. See Table 4.1 for an idea of reasonable combinations. For example, if you want more strength than endurance, use higher resistance and fewer

Table 4.1 Muscle Strength and Endurance Training

	Strength	Combination training	Endurance
Resistance (% maximum)	100%	75%	<50%
Repetitions	1	10 20	30
Sets	1–3		1–3
Frequency (days/week)	3	4 5	6

Example: If a professional player wants to develop primarily strength, he might design a program to work at 80% to 90% resistance for up to 3 sets of 5 to 10 repetitions and only do such training 3 or 4 times per week. On the other hand, a young player who wants some strength gain, but shouldn't expose his joints to heavy strength training, might select a combination training level of 50% to 60% resistance for 20 to 25 repetitions for 1 or 2 sets that he can do 5 days per week.

repetitions. Do the reverse if the player needs more endurance than strength.

Resistance • moderate to hard, 60 to 80%
Repetitions • 6 to 15
Sets • 3
Frequency • 3 to 5 times per week, determined by resistance

The following are some hints for designing strength/endurance programs:

• Most strength or endurance programs are done at a constant resistance and use the same number of repetitions for each set. When the third set can be done using the same number or repetitions as the first two sets, resistance for all sets is increased. Although it is more time-consuming, an effective combination program can also be designed as follows:

Set 1—12 to 15 reps at 50% resistance
Set 2—8 to 10 reps at 65% resistance
Set 3—6 reps at 80% resistance

• Rest between sets should allow for a sense of recovery from the previous set. Equal work to rest time is usually sufficient. Working in partners, where one exercises as the partner rests, is a useful system for strength/endurance workouts.

• Programs should include at least one exercise for each of the major muscle groups used in hockey (flexors and extensors of the legs, arms, and trunk). See Figure 4.1 for a more detailed list of the specific muscle groups. This usually requires at least 12 exercises. Additional exercises can be included for unusually weak areas or to get at particularly difficult angles, such as hip abductor and adductor exercises for the groin and lateral leg muscles. Work large muscle groups first.

• Programs must include exercises for pairs of muscles to maintain joint stability. For example, if a player wants to do sit-ups to strengthen his abdominal muscles, he must somewhere in his program include an exercise for back muscles. When a joint like the spine, knees, or elbows gets strong muscles on one side and those on the other side are left untrained, the joint is more susceptible to injury.

Figure 4.1
Weight training program.

(a) Sit-ups (abdominals). From back lying position with knees bent, grasp weight against chest. Curl up until arms touch thighs, then lower to starting position.

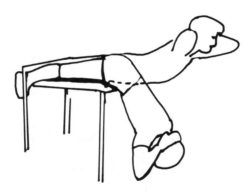

(b) Back lifts (lower back). From front lying position on a bench, with trunk overhanging, secure feet. Place hands on head or clasp weight to chest. Lower trunk toward floor, then return to original position.

Note. Do not hold breath while lifting weights. Breathe in during the effort phase of the exercise and breathe out during the recovery phase. Determine appropriate resistance and repetitions using the text and Table 4.1.

(c) Leg extension (quadriceps). From sitting position, secure weight at ankles. Stabilize rest of body. Extend knee to straight position, then lower to 90°.

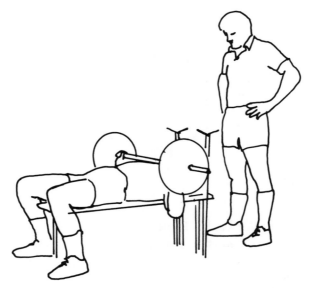

(d) Bench press (chest/shoulder). From a back lying position on a bench (feet on the floor), grasp weighted bar with palms up and hands shoulder-width apart. Lower bar to chest, then press up until elbows are extended.

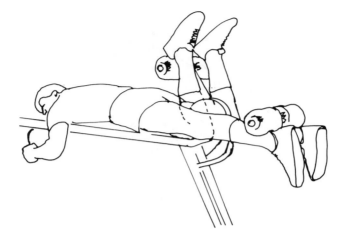

(e) Leg flexion (hamstrings). From a front lying position, secure weight at back of ankles. Stabilize rest of body. Bend knee until heels reach 90°, then lower heels until knee is straight.

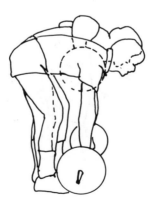

(f) Rowing (upper back). From front lying position on high bench or standing bent-over position, grasp weighted bar at floor. Lift bar to chest, then lower to floor.

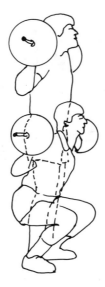

(g) Squats (quadriceps). From standing position with weighted bar across shoulders, place feet shoulder-width apart directly in line with path of knees. Lower hips until thighs are parallel to floor, then return to standing position. (Begin this exercise using light weights or partial squats, and progress very gradually. Strengthen the knees, don't strain them. A hockey player needs stable knees throughout their full range of movement.)

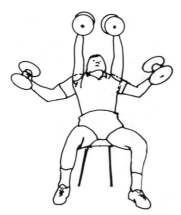

(h) Flys (chest/shoulder). From back lying position on bench (feet on floor), grasp dumbbells in straight arm position above chest. Lower dumbbells to T position, then return to above chest.

(i) Heel raises (calf). From standing position with weighted bar across shoulders, lift heels as high as possible off floor, then lower to floor. Use a raised block, if available, so heels can drop below floor level.

(j) Bicep curls (biceps). From standing position with back against a wall, grasp dumbbell with palm forward. Lift dumbbell from position at thigh toward the shoulder, then return to the thigh.

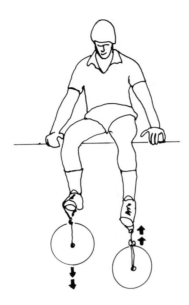

(k) Toe raises (ankle flexors). From sitting position on raised table, secure weight on toes. Lift toes toward shin, then lower as far as possible.

(l) Tricep curls (triceps). From standing position, grasp dumbbell in hand and extend arm overhead. Lower dumbbell toward back, then extend elbow until arm is straight.

(m) Wrist curls (wrist flexors). From sitting position with forearm resting on thigh, grasp dumbbell with palm up. Lift dumbbell toward forearm, then lower as far as possible.

(n) Wrist extension (wrist extensors). From sitting position with forearm resting on thigh, grasp barbell or dumbbell with palm down. Lift toward forearm, then lower toward knee.

• All strength/endurance programs should be followed by flexibility exercises for the same muscle groups. If muscles are left tight, they will lose their resilience and the range of motion through which they can be used.

• Strength/endurance begins to show improvement in 2 to 3 weeks, but it takes 6 to 12 weeks to reach a significant improvement for hockey. At that time, working out once or twice a week at the level attained will maintain the strength/endurance level achieved.

• A strength/endurance improvement program is best done in the off-season so that the base is established for working with specific skills in season. Then during the season, a player only needs to do a maintenance program and some specific on-ice work. This takes very little time away from working on hockey skills and strategies.

Sample Strength/Endurance Training Programs

The following examples are combination strength/endurance programs with slightly more emphasis on the strength factor because that is what is most useful in hockey. They can be modified to emphasize more endurance by manipulating the repetitions and sets, as indicated in the Principles section above.

Each sample program should be preceded by a good warm-up and followed by a cool-down and flexibility program (see chapter 8).

Figure 4.1 is an off-ice weight training program. It is illustrated using free weights, but it can be modified to suit Nautilus® or Universal® weight machines by selecting an exercise that uses the same muscle groups. Growing youths should only do this program using light weights and high repetitions.

An alternative for youths, or any team that does not wish to use weights, is the off-ice calisthenic program illustrated in Figure 4.2. This program requires minimal equipment, so it can be used by a team in a rink concourse, dressing room, or gymnasium. It can also be used by serious players at home or in a park as a maintenance or off-season program.

Muscle strength and endurance training can also be done on the ice. In fact, some on-ice work is advisable in season to make sure that specific muscle groups are trained. Figures 4.3 and 4.4 illustrate leg and arm drills designed more for development of strength. Figures 4.5 and 4.6 illustrate leg and arm drills designed more for endurance.

Levels are indicated in each of the training programs. Level 1 refers to targets for young, relatively inexperienced players. Level 2 applies to rather serious, early- to mid-teen players. Level 3 is for elite amateur and professional players.

Figure 4.2
Off-ice strength/endurance calisthenic program.

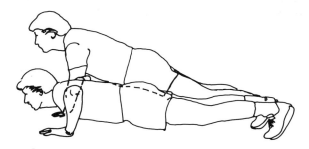

(a) Push-ups. From front lying position with knees bent and hands under shoulders, press body up until elbows are extended, then lower to starting position. Keep body straight throughout exercise.

(b) Twist sit-ups. From back lying position with hands on head, curl right shoulder toward left knee until elbow touches thigh. Return to starting position. Repeat motion with left shoulder toward right knee.

Note. Exercises can be done consecutively so that sets can be timed to monitor improvement. A 3- to 5-minute rest between sets allows sufficient recovery. Determine difficulty of the exercises and number of repetitions according to the previous text and Table 4.1.

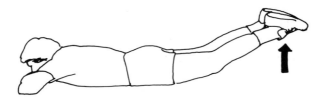

(c) Back leg lifts. From front lying position, lift straight legs as high as possible, then lower to floor. Do not swing legs.

(d) Burpees. From crouch position, extend feet back so that body is in straight push-up position. Return to crouch position, then extend straight up into maximal vertical jump. Return to crouch position.

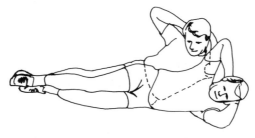

(e) Lateral curls. From side lying position with feet secured and hands on head, curl trunk up toward hip, then return to starting position. Repeat exercise for other side.

(f) Line jumps. From standing position between three lines, jump from either side of the inside line to either side of the outside lines. These can be two-foot or single-leg jumps.

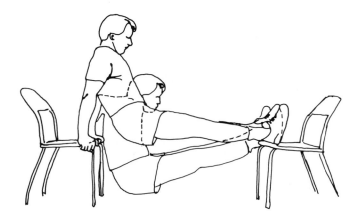

(g) Dips. From a sitting position on a chair with feet on another chair, lower hips from chair level as close to floor as possible, then return to starting position.

(h) Step-ups. From a standing position in front of a chair or high bench, step up onto the chair, then return to the floor one foot at a time. Switch lead leg halfway through repeats of the exercise.

Figure 4.3
On-ice leg strength drill.

Players work in pairs. Both players face the same direction with the front player bent so his hands are on his knees. The second player places his hands on the front player's hips and pushes him down the ice as the front player resists the forward motion. Players switch position at center ice.

Level 1. Front player gives mild resistance using his skate blades. Repeat 3 to 5 times.

Level 2. Front player gives moderate resistance. Repeat 4 to 8 times.

Level 3. Front player gives strong resistance. Repeat 6 to 10 times.

Figure 4.4
On-ice arm strength drill.

Players work in pairs. Place a puck behind one player. That player protects the puck while the second player tries to gain possession of the puck. The protecting player can only use his arms and stick to keep his opponent away from the puck. Players face each other all the time.

Level 1. Attacking player concentrates on keeping his stick on the ice. Repeat 3 to 5 times.

Level 2. Players attack aggressively. Repeat 4 to 8 times.

Level 3. Very aggressive play in the drill. Repeat 6 to 10 times.

Figure 4.5
On-ice leg endurance drill.

While skating the perimeter of the ice, players keep their left skate on the ice all the time while pushing only with the right. Keep two hands on the stick, with stick on the ice. Stress full extension every stride. Be sure to stride the corners. Repeat drill for the left leg.

Level 1. Take up to 15 to 20 strides with each skate. Repeat 3 times for each leg.

Level 2. Take 15 to 20 strides with each skate. Repeat 3 times for each leg.

Level 3. Take 20 to 30 strides with each skate. Repeat 3 times for each leg.

Figure 4.6
On-ice arm endurance drill.

Working in pairs, both players grasp the same hockey stick. On the coach's command, players wrestle to gain control of the stick.

Level 1. Wrestle for 12 to 15 seconds, 3 repeats.

Level 2. Wrestle for 15 to 20 seconds, 4 to 6 repeats.

Level 3. Wrestle for 20 to 25 seconds, 6 to 8 repeats.

Summary

Muscle strength and endurance work in combination to provide a base for players to better perform their skills. Strength and endurance are trained by manipulating resistance and number of repetitions according to whether more strength or more endurance is required. Improvement programs are most effective when done off-ice during the off-season. But, in season, on-ice maintenance is preferable to ensure specificity of training.

CHAPTER 5

Training for Flexibility

Flexibility is the ability of tissue around a joint to stretch and spring back. This elastic property of tissue provides some valuable assets for hockey players. Good flexibility minimizes the likelihood of strain-type injuries because the joints are capable of going safely through a wide range of motion. More power can be generated over a flexible joint because there is a greater range through which power can be built up, and the elasticity allows the muscle to snap back to its normal length with more force. For hockey, that means shots can be more forceful and skating strides can exert more power just from improved flexibility.

There are a variety of ways of doing flexibility training. *Static stretching* (move slowly to a position of maximum stretch, hold for a few seconds, then release and repeat; e.g., toe touches) is the most practiced technique. It provides the advantages described above if done following a workout. The *stretch-resistance* technique (carefully apply resistance while in a position of maximum stretch; e.g., same position as for toe touch, but a partner presses on your shoulders as you press against his pressure) is also effective for increasing elasticity around a joint if performed following exercises. The *stretch-relaxation* technique (which includes relaxation at the point of maximum stretch; e.g., assume same toe touch position, but let the tension drain from behind the knees or wherever it is felt) provides the additional benefit of reducing muscle soreness resulting from exercise.

Note that nonstatic, or *ballistic*, stretching (rotation through a range of motion or bouncing) is not particularly effective in providing any of the benefits listed for other flexibility training techniques. To improve elasticity, flexibility training should be done following a workout. But ballistic stretching exercises, such as arm circles, are beneficial before workouts because they "oil" the joint in preparation for all the work that is about to be undertaken. In addition, formal stretch positions that are likely to be encountered in the game or practice, such as goaltenders' splits, should be done in preparation for movements needed in the subsequent work session. However, both rotational and formal stretch position exercises should only be done after the muscles are well warmed up; muscles do not stretch easily when they are cold. And stretching at this time does not lead to significant improvements in flexibility. It only prepares the joints for subsequent activity.

Principles of Flexibility Training

The following principles will provide improvements in flexibility together with reducing the extent of muscle soreness if done following a work session. The stretch-relaxation technique is presented because it provides more benefits for the time invested.

Step 1—Stretch to a point of mild tension
Step 2—Hold that position and concentrate on relaxing any point(s) that feels tight (let all tension drain out of the muscles)
Step 3—Hold the relaxed position for at least 6 seconds (e.g., a slow count to 10)
Step 4—Repeat the exercise 2 more times
Frequency—Following every exercise session

The following are some hints for designing flexibility programs:

• If Step 3 is extended to beyond 30 seconds, Step 4 can be reduced to one repetition. Young players tend to have difficulty relaxing for long counts. The extended hold is better suited to older players.

• Include a stretching exercise for each of the major muscle groups used in playing hockey (calves, ankle flexors, quadriceps, hamstrings, groin, abdominals, lower back, sides, biceps, triceps, chest), such as those illustrated in Figure 5.1. Make sure that each muscle group has been both contracted and stretched at some point in the workout to ensure elasticity. Doing only one or the other predisposes the joint to injury.

• The frequency is based on the function of helping a muscle recover quickly after training or games. But flexibility can actually be maintained using this technique once per week if workouts are not too intense.

• Flexibility shows improvement very quickly (a few weeks), although best results are obtained in 8 to 10 weeks. Because flexibility is best done following workouts, even when no further improvement is necessary, the most practical maintenance program is to do one repetition of each exercise using the stretch-relaxation technique.

• It is important to do flexibility training in conjunction with any strength/endurance work. For this reason, a flexibility improvement program is best done in the off-season, with a switch to a maintenance program in season.

Sample Flexibility Training Programs

Flexibility programs, for the sake of improvement, are best done off-ice. Some stretching can be done on-ice as part of a warm-up or cool-down (see chapter 8 for examples), but hockey equipment and the slippery surface interfere with good flexibility training. Figure 5.1 illustrates a complete flexibility training program that can be done in a hallway or dressing room. It should be done immediately following the practice or game, and players should remove skates and pads. The program takes 10 to 15 minutes as an improvement program and about 5 minutes as a maintenance program.

Figure 5.1
Off-ice flexibility program.

Do either exercises a, b, and c or d and e, then proceed with all of the remaining exercises. "Hold" indicates the position for relaxed draining of the tension created by the stretch.

(a) Long sit. Point toes toward knees. Hold. Press stomach to thighs, then drop head toward knees. Hold.

(b) Straddle sit. Press stomach toward right thigh, then drop head toward knee. Hold. Repeat toward left thigh and knee. Hold. Repeat straight forward. Hold.

(c) Reverse hurdle sit. Sit with bottoms of feet together. Press down on knees. Hold. Extend one leg forward. Press stomach toward thigh, then drop head toward knee. Hold. Lie back. Press small of back toward floor and hold as gravity works groin. Repeat from beginning for other leg.

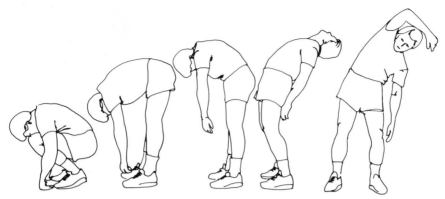

(d) Squat stretch. Relax totally in a full squat position. Then slowly press heels to floor and extend knees until legs are straight. Hold. Slowly straighten spine as if working one vertebra at a time. Continue to pass through the vertical position to a back-bend position. Hold. Slowly straighten spine again as if working one vertebra at a time. Bend to the left. Hold. Straighten up as before. Bend to right. Hold. Straighten as previously. Twist shoulders to left. Hold. Twist to right. Hold.

(e) Straddle stretch. Dip to a low lateral lunge position, keeping both feet flat on the floor pointing straight forward. Hold. Grasp ankle, then extend same knee until straight, keeping head as close to knee as possible. Hold. Move trunk to center position and press elbows as close to the floor as possible. Hold. Repeat sequence to other side.

(f) Forward lunge. Dip as close to the floor as possible, keeping the back erect and the knee of the extended leg straight. Hold. Repeat reversing leg positions.

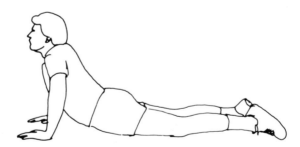

(g) Drop hip stretch. From a front lying position, press shoulders as high off the floor as possible while relaxing the trunk to keep the hips on the floor. Hold.

(h) Gluteal stretch. Sit with one leg extended and the other crossed over it at the knee, with the foot placed on the floor beside and parallel to the knee. Press the raised knee toward the opposite shoulder. Hold. Repeat for other leg.

(i) Shoulder stretches. Wrap one arm around front of neck as the other arm presses at the elbow. Hold. Reach overhead and down the back as the other arm presses down at the elbow. Hold. Place hand on wall at shoulder height, then turn body away from hand. Hold.

(j) Calf stretch. Bend forward to place hands on floor, then extend one leg back as far as possible. Slowly roll back until the back heel can be pressed to the floor, then dip knee keeping the heel on the floor. Hold. Repeat for other leg.

(k) Lower back relaxer. From back lying position, press lower back toward the floor. Hold. Draw one leg up to chest. Hold. Repeat for other leg, then repeat using both legs.

Summary

Flexibility is an asset to a hockey player for injury reduction, power generation, and reduction of muscle tension and soreness. It is best trained in the off-season using a stretch-relaxation technique following every workout. Maintenance is most effective when still done following every practice and game, but less time is required. It is important to couple muscle stretching exercises with contracting exercises to retain elasticity.

CHAPTER 6

Training for Quickness and Speed

Quickness and speed are what hockey is all about. Hockey is a fast game in which fractions of seconds count for everyone. The faster a player can apply his skills, the better he will be. Goaltenders, of course, need both foot and hand quickness (alactic energy) to maneuver and stop shots from all angles. Forwards are most effective if they have good wrist quickness for shots, good leg quickness for agility, and ongoing speed (lactic energy) to go up and down the ice. Defensemen need the quick hands for interfering with shots and passes, as well as foot quickness and speed to jockey for position and play strong all shift.

Alactic conditioning bolsters the amount of chemicals (ATP/PC) in the muscle that allow explosive action to occur so a player can move more quickly. Lactic conditioning improves a player's fast fuel storage (CHO) and his ability to withstand large amounts of LA so it does not limit his speed so quickly.

When a player is conditioning either of these energy supply systems, the nervous system is an important factor. Different nerves service anaerobic (alactic and lactic) as opposed to predominantly aerobic muscle cells. They are called fast twitch and slow twitch muscle cells, respectively. Because different nerve pathways are used by the different cell types, the training intensities (pace) noted below must be strictly maintained. If a player trains at a reduced intensity, he will use totally different nerves and muscle cells. The result will be that his anaerobic abilities will not improve to any great extent in the cells that can do him the most good.

Principles of Quickness (Alactic) Training

All of the following elements must be included to improve a player's anaerobic alactic energy supply system.

Pace	• maximum, "guts out"
Duration	• 5 to 10 seconds
Rest Intervals	• 5 to 6 times the work time
Total Amount	• 6 to 12 repeats
Frequency	• 2 to 6 times per week

The following are some hints for designing quickness training programs:

• The "guts-out" pace is critical if the right muscle cells are to be activated. The rest intervals are designed to provide sufficient rest that the "guts-out" effort can be maintained for the necessary number of repeats. If players begin to slow down, it is best to increase the rest intervals or cut the number of repeats rather than continue the drill at a slower pace. The latter would be a waste of time because the wrong muscle cells and nerves would be used. Start with few repeats and gradually increase the number as players are able to sustain the effort after 50 seconds' rest.

• The explosive energy system is very easily trained, so that only a couple of work sessions per week will result in some improvement. More work sessions, however, seem to result in faster improvement, so if time is available (10 minutes), some anaerobic alactic training could be done at every practice.

• Quickness improves rapidly, according to practice frequency. Once an appropriate level of quickness is attained, it can be maintained by doing one session per week at the intensity and number of repeats finally accomplished. That may be, for example, 8-second efforts followed by 40-second rests, repeated 10 times.

• Explosive power training can be done during any part of a player's season. It can be trained more effectively if an aerobic base is developed first. During the season, it becomes important to use very specific on-ice alactic drills to ensure specificity of training in the hockey muscles.

Sample Conditioning Drills for Quickness

Anaerobic alactic training can be done on or off the ice. On-ice work is most crucial for maintenance during the season. The off-season and early season are ideal times to do off-ice work on quickness.

Remember that all players can benefit from both quick hands and quick feet. Drills for both should be included in a conditioning program. Figure 6.1 illustrates an on-ice alactic drill for the legs. Figure 6.2 is also on-ice, but for the arms. Figures 6.3 and 6.4 are excellent off-ice exercises for developing explosive energy in the legs and arms, respectively. Remember that intensity is the key factor in all these drills. Levels 1 to 3 are included in the drills as guides for pre-teens, early teens, and elite and professional players respectively.

Figure 6.1
On-ice leg quickness drill.

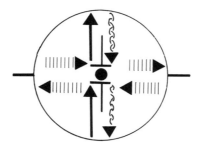

Use a faceoff circle. Start on the dot facing the boards. Face the same direction throughout the drill. Skate forward to the edge of the circle, stop, skate backward to the dot, stop, sidestep to the edge of the circle to the right, stop, sidestep back to the dot, stop, backskate to the back of the circle, stop, skate forward to the dot, stop, sidestep to the left side of the circle, stop, sidestep back to the dot, stop, skate to the top of the circle. Repeat sequence for 10 seconds, then rest 50 seconds. Players can work four to a circle with one player doing the drill at a time.

Level 1. Repeat 4 to 6 times. Pylons may be used to make the distance shorter in each direction so all directions are used in the 10 seconds.

Level 2. Repeat 5 to 10 times.

Level 3. Repeat 8 to 12 times.

Figure 6.2
On-ice arm quickness drill.

Player is positioned near the boards with a puck. Select a target on the boards at ice level. Shoot the puck at the target from wherever it rebounds, as many times as possible in a 10-second period.

Level 1. Have player stay close to the boards to reduce difficulty.

Level 2. Player selects a second target about 1 foot off the ice. Alternate shots at the two targets.

Level 3. Use 10 to 15 pucks in front of a net. Select 3 or 4 scoring spots as targets (no goaltender). Rapid-fire pucks at alternating targets.

Figure 6.3
Off-ice leg quickness exercise.

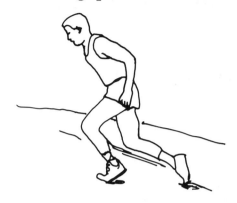

Use an incline (e.g., hill, stairs). Drive as hard and quickly as possible up the incline for a maximum of 10 to 15 long strides. Return slowly to the starting point to allow appropriate rest before repeating.

Level 1. Use a flat surface or gradual incline. Repeat 4 to 6 times.

Level 2. Use a steeper incline. Repeat 5 to 10 times.

Level 3. Use long, driving strides (e.g., 3 steps at a time when using stairs). Repeat 8 to 12 times.

Figure 6.4
Off-ice arm quickness exercise.

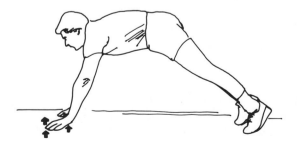

Start in the push-up position. Push away from the floor as hard as possible. Hands should leave the floor. Repeat as many times as possible in 5 to 10 seconds. Rest. Repeat.

Level 1. Repeat as described 4 to 6 times.

Level 2. Push off the floor and clap hands on chest while in the air. Repeat 5 to 10 times.

Level 3. Increase resistance by elevating the feet. Tap chest in the air. Repeat 8 to 12 times.

Principles of Speed (Lactic) Training

All of the following elements must be included to get improvement in the anaerobic lactic energy supply system.

Pace	• near maximum, as hard as possible
Duration	• 40 to 90 seconds
Rest Interval	• equal to or double the work time
Total Amount	• 4 to 10 repeats
Frequency	• once per 48 hours

The following are some hints for designing speed training programs:

• Heart rate can be used to check pace in speed training. A player would take a pulse count for 10 seconds immediately after the second or third repeat of the drill. (Start counting with 0, 1, 2 . . .) Multiply the number of beats by 6. This value should be above 200 minus the player's age. Heart rates above 200 are common in players under 20 years of age. However, an old timer's anaerobic heart rate would be closer to 180. See Table 6.1 for target training heart rates for all ages.

• Rest intervals should be adjusted to allow the intensity to be sustained at near maximal levels. If the pace drops, the incorrect muscle cells, nerve pathways, and chemicals will be used, and the time spent training will be wasted. Similarly, the target number of repeats should be increased only as the pace can be sustained with

Table 6.1 Age-Adjusted Target Training Heart Rates.

Heart rate (beats per minute)

Age (years)	10	20	30	40	50	60	70
210	Δ						
200		Δ					
190	*		Δ				
180		*		Δ			
170			*		Δ		
160	•			*		Δ	
150		•			*		Δ
140			•			*	
130				•			*
120					•		
110						•	
100							•

Age (years)

Between • and * = Aerobic target training range
Between * and Δ = Anaerobic lactic (speed) target training range

equal rest intervals. For example, if players perform the fourth repeat of a speed drill with an obvious drop in pace, either take a longer rest before doing the fifth repeat, or stop at the fourth repeat and make that the target until players can perform the fourth repetition at a pace close to that of the third repeat.

• Anaerobic lactic training drains the muscles of their CHO stores and imposes rather severe wear and tear on the muscles and joints. For these reasons, it is recommended that heavy lactic training not be done more frequently than once per 48 hours. That time allows CHO stores to be refilled and muscles to recover more completely. Two or three lactic training sessions per week are sufficient for improving the system. It is also recommended that lactic training not be done the same day as heavy strength training due to the wear and tear both exert on muscles.

• It takes 6 weeks or more to get major improvements in the anaerobic alactic system, depending mostly on the aerobic condition of a player. A once-a-week maintenance program can then be conducted, using the same pace and number of repeats that were done at the highest training level attained. If a player was doing 8 repetitions of a 60-second all-out drill with 60 seconds' rest, then that is what he should do once a week to maintain his speed-producing energy.

• Speed training is only worth doing in the off-season if players already have a good aerobic base. Most training to develop the aerobic base is done in the off-season. So lactic training is left for the early season and maintenance can be done by midseason. This is an acceptable practice because anaerobic lactic energy is very specific to the muscle groups used, so specificity of training for hockey must be accommodated during the season anyway.

Sample Speed Training Drills

Anaerobic lactic training can be done on or off the ice. On-ice work is crucial for the in-season maintenance program. Off-ice work is useful during either the pre- or early season. Speed takes time to develop and it is lost quite easily, so players must work very hard on the intensity so that time spent on lactic drills is well invested.

Figure 6.5 is an example of an on-ice lactic drill. It is a very demanding exercise for players. Figure 6.6 illustrates a similar concept for training speed using a field or gymnasium. Levels are provided as guidelines for using the drills with progressively older, more experienced players.

Figure 6.5
On-ice speed drill.

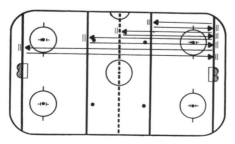

Players line up on the goal line. On signal, they skate as hard as possible to the blue line, back to the goal line, to center, back to the goal line, to the far blue line, back to the goal line, to the far goal line, and back to the goal line. Rest. Repeat. Players can work in two waves, with the second group starting when the first group finishes. This allows equal rest intervals.

Level 1. Use lines that allow a 30- to 60-second effort. Repeat 4 to 6 times.

Level 2. Use lines that allow a 40- to 70-second effort. Repeat 4 to 8 times.

Level 3. Use lines that allow a 60- to 90-second effort. Repeat 6 to 10 times.

Figure 6.6
Off-ice speed drill.

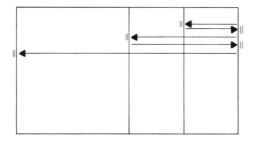

Use a playfield or lined gym floor. Start players on an end line. Sprint a sequence of lines, of gradually increasing lengths, back and forth to the starting line. Finish at the opposite end line and walk back to the starting line. Rest. Repeat. Players can go in 2 or 3 waves.

Level 1. Use lines that allow a 30- to 60-second effort. Repeat 4 to 6 times.

Level 2. Use lines that allow a 40- to 70-second effort. Repeat 4 to 8 times.

Level 3. Use lines that allow a 60- to 90-second effort. Repeat 6 to 10 times.

Summary

Both the quickness and the overall speed of a hockey player can be improved significantly by proper conditioning. Training must be very specific to the muscles and nerves required for hockey. Thus intensity is a critical factor. If explosive energy is used in training, then quickness will improve. If sustained high energy is used in training, then the player will improve his ability to retain high speeds. Quickness and speed training time is most productive if players establish a good aerobic base first. Most of the improvement program should be conducted in the early season.

CHAPTER 7

Training for Endurance and Recovery

Endurance and recovery are the conditioning cornerstones of a hockey player's game. If he has good endurance, he can use his skills to their maximum each time out on the ice. If fatigue sets in, accuracy and speed deteriorate and his skills become ineffective. A good aerobic system wards off fatigue because the heart is stronger and better at circulating the blood and fuels necessary to keep going.

A good aerobic system also lets a player take advantage of the times he gets to coast or sit down during the game. A strong heart and good circulatory system provide better flushing of waste chemicals, such as LA, and better delivery of the goods that are needed to refill the ATP supplies, such as CHO and fats. If a player recovers quickly, he can use the alactic and lactic energy supply systems over and over. That means he can use more quickness and speed throughout the game.

Training to improve endurance and recovery is rather time-consuming, but specificity is not as important as for anaerobic training. Running, skipping, biking, rowing, rollerskating, and many other total body activities will challenge the heart, lungs, and circulatory system. Ice time does not have to be committed frequently. Occasional on-ice sessions should be conducted to include some specificity of training.

Principles of Aerobic Conditioning

All of the following elements must be included to get improvement in aerobic conditioning.

Pace	• brisk, moderate
Duration	• 15 to 40 minutes
Rest Intervals	• 30 seconds maximum
Frequency	• 3 to 6 times per week

The following are some hints for designing aerobic training programs:

• Pace is best determined by doing a heart rate check after about 5 minutes of exercise. Pulse is counted for 10 seconds (start the count with 0, 1, 2 . . .), then multiply by 6. Beginning target training heart rates should be 170 minus the player's age. As the player improves, work up to a heart rate of 200 minus his age. See Table 6.1 in the previous chapter for aerobic target training heart rates for all ages. Younger players could do a 6-second heart rate count, then put a 0 for the value. This avoids problems with mathematical ability, although it is a little less accurate.

• Ideally, a player should be able to exercise continuously for the duration specified. However, if players are just beginning to get in shape, 15 minutes nonstop may be too much. In that case, the total time can be broken into short segments that alternate the brisk pace for 2 to 4 minutes with an easy pace for 30 seconds. As players improve, shorten the rest intervals to 20 seconds, then 10, and ultimately no rest. Rest does not necessarily imply ''do nothing.'' Changing pace from running to jogging or from jogging to walking is appropriate rest.

• The frequency range means that the least a player can do to improve his aerobic system is three training sessions per week. Four or five sessions allow improvement to occur more quickly as long as overload is carefully applied. Six times per week does not seem to provide any advantage over five. Some players prefer to establish a daily exercise habit, but it is not recommended that a player be encouraged to do the same training regime 7 days per week. The body needs a day to recover and rebuild as it adapts to the training stimulus. If a player insists on a daily habit, then vary the type and pace of at least two of the seven sessions per week. For example, swim instead of run or bike, or do an aerobic calisthenic circuit.

• To maintain a satisfactory level of aerobic conditioning after you have achieved it, keep the pace and duration of the level you have attained, and reduce the frequency to once or twice a week. For example, players may have been running 20 minutes continuously at a strong (HR 200 − age) pace by the end of training camp. If that were the level of aerobic conditioning they chose to maintain, they could then skate for 20 minutes once a week after practice at that same strong pace to maintain their level of aerobic conditioning.

• Because endurance and recovery are so important for training other muscle and energy systems, aerobic energy is one of the first things to establish in a hockey player. For this reason, aerobic training is best done in the off-season. If that is not practical, aerobics should be developed as soon as practices begin. It takes 6 to 12 weeks to significantly improve the aerobic energy system. Because it is so time-consuming, it is most convenient to be on a maintenance program by the time games begin.

Sample Aerobic Training Programs

The most economical way to improve or maintain aerobic conditioning during on-ice practices is to combine the principles outlined above with a variety of simple skills that need to be worked on anyway. This combination is often referred to as a flow drill. Because the intensity of aerobic training is just moderate, many skills will not interfere with the intensity requirement. Figure 7.1 is an example of an on-ice aerobic training flow drill.

Figure 7.2 presents suggestions for conducting an off-ice aerobic training drill, according to what equipment and facility is available. Levels 1 to 3 are included as guides to adjust aerobic training to suit youth, teens, and previously trained players.

Figure 7.1
Aerobic flow drill.

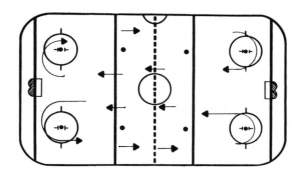

Players skate down the middle of the ice and return along the boards, alternating board sides each time. All players skate continuously at a brisk pace. Coach blows the whistle to change activity from (a) through (e) as the players continue to move through the pattern. Activities should last 1 to 4 minutes according to players' skill level. The drill must last at least 15 minutes in total.

(a) Forward striding. Coach monitors correct posture and stride.

(b) Backward skating.

(c) Half and half. Players skate forward around the corners and backward between the blue lines.

(d) Agility. Players do three strides left then three right between the blue lines.

(e) Pivots. Players pivot at each blue line, one to the left, the next to the right.

Level 1. Do the drill as described without pucks. Then repeat (a), (c), and (d) with pucks, as players are capable of handling pucks and still keeping a brisk intensity.

Level 2. Do the complete drill as described once, then a second time using pucks. Pylons can be used for (d) to increase the difficulty.

Level 3. Use pucks throughout the drill. Add (f) (board passes), as players come up the wings. Keep the pace very brisk.

Figure 7.2
Off-ice aerobic conditioning.

Use running, biking, rowing, or skipping, indoors or out. If players run around an arena concourse, change direction at halftime. The pace should be moderate to strong for a minimum of 15 minutes. A combination of the activities listed could also be used to provide variety.

Level 1. Run for 2 minutes, then walk for 30 seconds (brisk pace). Alternate the two paces for 15 minutes of activity in total. The rest interval can be reduced as the 15 minutes becomes easier.

Level 2. Run 3 minutes, then jog 30 seconds. Alternate the two paces for 15 to 20 minutes. Jog times can gradually be reduced, then eliminated.

Level 3. Run 15 minutes continuously. Then break the additional time into 2 to 3 minutes of stronger efforts alternating with 30 seconds of moderately paced efforts until the drill has lasted 20 to 30 minutes in total.

Summary

Aerobic training is the base from which other aspects of conditioning are made more effective. Because a hockey player needs all aspects of conditioning, plus endurance and recovery, aerobic conditioning is a fundamental necessity. It is best to develop aerobics during the off-season because ice time need not be committed, and it is best to have a good aerobic conditioning level before practices begin so practices can be more effective.

CHAPTER 8

Other Training Tips

Conditioning needs can be met by adhering to the principles outlined in chapters 4 to 7. However, there are a few other tips that
can be incorporated in a training program to make it safer, more
effective, and less time-consuming. For example, most people know
that a warm-up should be used at the outset of any game or practice.
Similarly, it is wise to cool down following a hard work session.
But how do you know when a player is warmed up enough to work
hard or cooled down enough to stop?

And where does a team get all the time it takes to do all the
training it should do? Many teams get little enough ice and practice
time as it is to do the skills and strategy work they want. And how
do you add to that when individual players have weaknesses that
extra conditioning could improve?

Warm-Ups

A warm-up is supposed to gradually heat the body up, then generally and specifically prepare muscles and joints for subsequent
activity. The key points are *gradual heating* and *general and specific
preparation.*

A good warm-up includes three distinct steps. The first is total
body movement, such as jogging or skating, that can increase in
pace from very easy to moderate. None of these activities should
be at maximal pace or range of movement. This step is designed
simply to generate some heat in the muscles and to get the heart
and circulatory system prepared for activity.

The second step is loose, rotating range of motion exercises, such as arm or leg swings. These exercises should begin well within the maximal range of motion and gradually become more complete. This step is designed to lubricate the joints so they are prepared to handle the jarring of subsequent exercise.

The third step should include actions and paces that mirror those that will be required in the game or practice. These activities generally include maximal pace and range of motion. For a goaltender, that means doing the splits. Other players should do some maximal, static stretches for the groin and shoulders and a few sprints.

All three phases should be included in every warm-up regardless of the amount of time available. Ideally, a warm-up should take at least 15 minutes and Step 1 should bring a player to sensing some heat on his brow. Both Steps 1 and 2 should begin with very loose, comfortable levels of the activity and gradually increase the intensity and the range of motion.

Figure 8.1 provides a sample warm-up that could be done on the ice before a game or practice. Figure 8.2 illustrates an off-ice warm-up that can be used before a dryland training session.

In summary, a good warm-up includes gradual heating up of the muscles, then lubrication of the joints, and finally, simulation of specific actions involved in the sport. These three steps should be done before all practices and games.

Figure 8.1
On-ice warm-up.

Step 1. Skate 4 to 6 laps of the ice, starting with a very easy pace and gradually increasing the speed of each successive lap to finish with 2 to 3 laps of alternately sprinting the blue lines, then sprinting the corners.

(a)

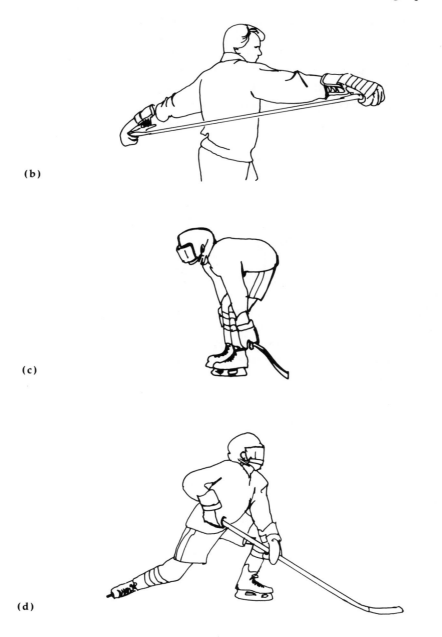

(b)

(c)

(d)

Step 2. Still moving around the perimeter of the ice, slowly do neck rotations to the right and the left (a). Then place the stick across the shoulders and rotate to the right and left. Move the stick across the upper back then lower back (b) for left and right rotations. Lower stick behind the legs to touch the heels (c). Hold. Straighten up and repeat the rotating and stretch sequence. Then, alternating right and left legs, dip to stretch the groin area (d), using a partial dip first, then the complete stretch, over 3 to 5 dips. Keep the upper body erect when doing groin stretches. Roll and shrug the shoulders.

(e)

Step 3. Skaters do puckhandling and sprints as they skate the perimeter. Goaltenders move to center ice and do specific stretches and some quick lateral movements. Skaters then shoot pucks on goaltenders in net, starting with long shots, then shorter, harder shots (e).

Figure 8.2
Off-ice warm-up.

(a)

Step 1. Jog, skip rope, or run (a) on the spot to gradually raise the body temperature (3 to 5 minutes).

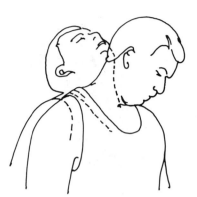

(b)

(c)

(d)

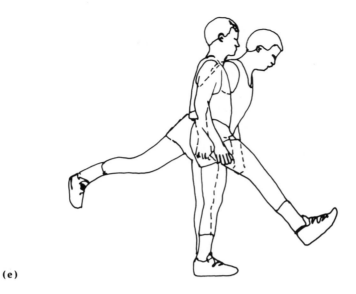

(e)

Step 2. Rotate each joint from the top of the body down (i.e., neck [b], shoulders [c], wrists, trunk [d], hips [e], knees, ankles). Do rotations in both directions.

Step 3. Do a light calisthenic series (10 to 15 repeats) that includes each of the major muscle groups, except legs (e.g., push-ups, sit-ups, back leg lifts, dips). Finish with 3 to 5 short sprints (50 meters/yards) with a walk back. Stretch out (static technique) any muscle groups that feel tight.

Cool-Downs

Cooling down after heavy exercise is a good habit to get into. It initiates more effective recovery mechanisms, and it prevents blood from pooling in the legs. When blood pools, players feel dizzy or light-headed. This can be dangerous for fast-growing youths and older players, particularly those with weak hearts.

An actual cool-down should involve total body exercise, such as walking or skating, that gradually changes in pace from moderate to very easy. A 5-minute cool-down is usually adequate. A player can take a pulse count to check. When the heart rate is back below 120 for young athletes or under 100 for athletes over 25 years of age, then the cool-down is sufficient.

Another activity that is often considered to be part of cool-down is flexibility work. Stretching does not actually cool the body, but it should be included as a second step in a cool-down for two reasons. It is the best time to improve flexibility because the muscles are warm and consequently will stretch more easily than when they are cold. Improvement can then be greater. Second, stretch-relaxation flexibility work helps reduce muscle soreness that may result from the workout, and it facilitates relaxation in the muscles, which promotes recovery.

A good cool-down for hockey would simply be to skate the perimeter of the ice for a few minutes. Each lap should get slower with looser skating. Some rotation exercises, such as those used in the warm-up, could be performed. When heart rate lowers, players should leave the ice and remove skates and equipment. Stretch-relaxation exercises (see chapter 5) should then be performed in the dressing room or hallway.

An effective cool-down should include a gradual decline in total body activity level from moderate to loose and easy. It should conclude with stretch-relaxation flexibility work.

Time Savers

Practice time often seems to be at a premium for hockey teams. Either too little ice time is available or the game and players' schedules leave little time for practice. And there is so much hockey to cover. How can a team get all the skills, conditioning, and strategy work done in the little time that is available?

There are two good ways to save time and still accomplish what is needed for skills, conditioning, and strategies. One technique is to train more than one aspect of conditioning at a time. This leaves more time for skill and strategy work.

The technique of combined training is often referred to as circuit training. To make it successful, combine the principles for the items you want to condition. For example, the principles of aerobic conditioning can be combined with quickness and muscle strength/endurance principles. Recognize that the speed of improvement will be compromised slightly because the optimum level of the principles may be modified to fit the circuit. But combination training is much better than no training at all.

A sample combination program for training quickness and speed on ice is illustrated in Figure 8.3. The changing number of laps allows the drill to evolve from alactic to lactic system training.

Figure 8.4 presents an off-ice circuit that is an all-in-one (except flexibility) circuit. It trains muscle strength/endurance for each of the major muscle groups and quickness for the upper and lower body in such combination that aerobic principles are met, and it finishes off with speed training. Note that all this is accomplished in as little as 20 minutes.

A second technique for saving time is to combine training requirements with on-ice skill drills. Then both skill work and conditioning are accomplished at one time, leaving more time for strategy work. This technique can be used effectively for conditioning any of the energy supply systems or strength/endurance. Close attention must be paid to the pace requirement when doing alactic and lactic system drills.

Figure 8.3
On-ice combination speed and quickness drill.

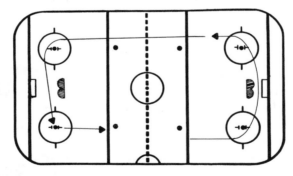

Divide the team into four groups, placing one group at each of the neutral zone faceoff dots. Pull the goal nets toward the center of the ice so that players can skate the perimeter of the ice staying outside all the faceoff dots. Group 1 skates the perimeter of the ice and stops at the original faceoff dot. As they pass Group 2's dot, Group 2 skates the perimeter of the ice. Groups 3 and 4 follow in sequence. Group 1 follows Group 4 for repeats. Change directions for the drill after a number of repeats.

Level 1. First repeat is 1/2 lap easy, 1/2 lap at top speed. Second repeat is full lap at top speed. Alternate these two repeats for 6 to 8 laps.

Level 2. Groups do 1 lap on the first repeat, 2 laps on the second repeat, and 3 laps on the third repeat. Go through this sequence 3 to 5 times. All laps should be done at top speed.

Level 3. Skate a sequence of 1, 2, 3, 2, 1 laps, 3 to 5 times. All laps are at top speed, including skating the corners.

Figure 8.4
Off-ice conditioning circuit.

Use a gym, field, or arena concourse. Post a list of the following exercises on the wall at one end, where there is room for players to do the exercises. The sequence is for players to run at a moderate pace, approximately 2 minutes (1 or 2 laps), then do one exercise from the list. Run 2 more minutes, then do the next exercise on the list, until the player works through the whole list of exercises. This part of the drill is nonstop and the sequence can be repeated more than once through. The sequence should be adjusted to last 12 to 15 minutes. Immediately following the last sequence, players run laps of sprint 100 steps, then walk 50 steps for 3 to 6 repeats.

Exercises:

(a) Power push-ups (sequence of 2 normal, 1 clap hands)

(b) Twist sit-ups (alternate to one side each sit-up)

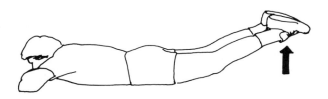

(c) Back leg lifts

(d) Tuck jumps (sequence of 2 bounces, 1 tuck jump)

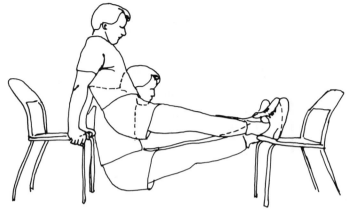

(e) Dips

Level 1. Do 10 to 15 repeats of each exercise and only 2 or 3 repeats of the final sprints.

Level 2. Do 15 to 20 repeats of each exercise. Go twice through the circuit. Include sprints as described at the end of the second sequence.

Level 3. Do 20 to 30 repeats of each exercise, 3 times through the circuit. Include all final sprints.

Figure 8.5 is an example of a combination skill and conditioning drill. This drill works quickness for upper and lower body while practicing skating, puckhandling, and shooting skills. Similarly, Figure 8.6 illustrates aerobic training, which is combined with skating, puck control, and passing/receiving skills. Figure 8.7 combines speed training with passing and shooting work. Figure 8.8 combines quickness training with skating, pass receiving, and shooting skills.

There often seems to be too little practice time for all the things that need to be done in hockey. To make more efficient use of time, coaches can design drills to combine the training of more than one component of conditioning at a time, and they can design drills that combine skill work with conditioning principles. Many of a coach's favorite skill drills can be modified to meet training requirements to provide combination skill/conditioning drills. This approach also provides the subtle benefit of ensuring that practice drills are done at game pace.

Figure 8.5

Combination quickness and skating, puckhandling, and shooting circuit.

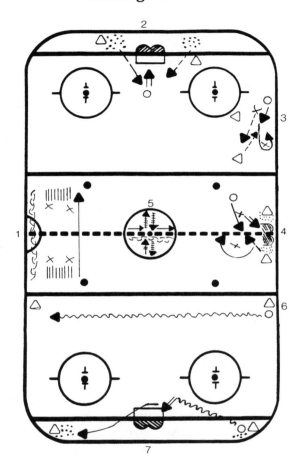

Put all skaters in groups of three. Assign each goaltender to a net. Designate different drill stations over the entire ice surface, with each assigned a number. Have enough stations that there can be one station per group. (If there are seven groups of players, there should be seven stations.) A whistle blows to start and stop each exercise and to change stations. Players rotate clockwise through the different stations. Each player in a group does the drill for 10 seconds at each station before the group moves on to the next station (30 seconds).

Station 1. Player faces the same direction all the time as he skates the perimeter of a pylon box as quickly as possible.

Station 2. Two players with pucks stand at the side of a net with the third player in his most common shooting position. Shooter receives passes alternating from the other two players and shoots on goal as quickly as possible.

Station 3. Place 2 pylons 8 to 10 feet apart. One player skates a figure-eight pattern around them. The other two players stand facing the skater, each with a puck, and alternately pass and receive a pass from the skater as he goes between the pylons.

Station 4. Use a figure-eight pattern as in Station 3, but place pylons in front of the net. The skater fires the puck on goal as soon as he receives each pass.

Station 5. Skater starts on the faceoff dot of the center ice circle. He faces the same direction all the time as he skates to the top of the circle, stops, backskates to the dot, stops, sidesteps to the right side of the circle, stops, sidesteps to the dot, stops, backskates to the back of the circle, stops, forward to the dot, stops, sidesteps to left of the circle, stops, back to the center dot. Repeat until time is up.

Station 6. Using the width of the ice, two players line up on one side of the boards, one with a puck. The third player is on the opposite side of the ice against the boards. The skater with the puck skates the width of the ice as quickly as possible and gives the puck to the player on that side. He carries it back across the ice and exchanges the puck with the next player. This continues as many times as possible for the complete 30-second period at this station.

Station 7. Use a goaltender and a net. Two players start in one corner and one in the other. Pucks are in both corners. One of the two players skates out of his corner with a puck and skates quickly in on goal for a shot. Then he goes to the opposite corner and the player in that corner repeats. This exchange continues for the complete 30 seconds of the drill.

Level 1. Some stations may have to be modified to reduce the level of skill required. Intensity must be retained.

Level 2. Perform as described.

Level 3. Repeat entire circuit twice.

Figure 8.6

Combination aerobic and skating, puck control, and passing/receiving drill.

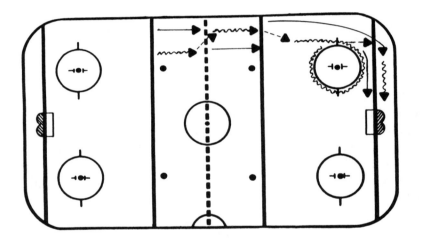

Players skate continuously around the perimeter of the ice at a brisk pace. Then players pick up pucks as they pass center and work on lateral movement and skating the corners. On the coach's command, they then pair up and pass both pucks back and forth as they skate the perimeter. Players then leave the pucks at center ice and change the skating pattern to skate each faceoff circle (alternating one clockwise, second counterclockwise). Keeping this pattern, players then pick up a puck as they skate the circles. Lastly, players pair up again, but with only one puck per pair. Player with puck skates the first circle. As he comes off that circle, he passes to his partner who takes the puck and skates the second circle, passing off as he completes the circle. The receiving player continues along the perimeter until he gets the pass, so that some passes are relatively short, and some will be long. The puck carrier has to skate heads up to know where to pass. The drill should last 15 to 20 minutes. Pylons can be added to increase difficulty for more advanced players.

Figure 8.7

Combination speed and passing and shooting drill.

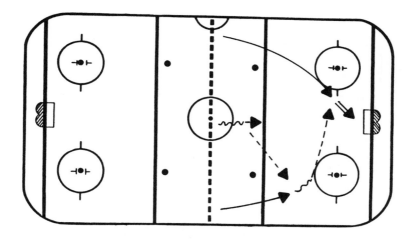

Use a goaltender. Three players start on the center ice line with a puck. All three go hard in on goal. Each player has to touch the puck before it is shot on goal. After the shot, all three return to the center line as quickly as possible, get another puck, and repeat the attack.

Level 1. Perform drill for 30 to 60 seconds. Rest 1 to 2 minutes. Repeat 4 to 6 times.

Level 2. Perform drill for 40 to 70 seconds. Rest 60 to 90 seconds. Repeat 5 to 8 times.

Level 3. Perform drill for 60 to 90 seconds. Rest 60 to 90 seconds. Repeat 6 to 10 times.

Figure 8.8

Combination quickness and skating, pass receiving, and shooting drill.

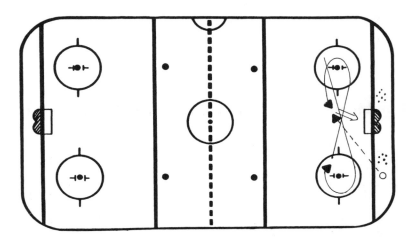

One player skates a figure eight using the two end zone faceoff dots so that he skates toward the goal through the slot. Another player feeds him a pass each time he approaches the slot, which the skater immediately releases on goal. The passer should alternate sides of the net he feeds from with each set of passes. One set is as many passes as the shooter can receive in 10 seconds. Skating pace is as fast as possible (no coasting around dots). Two passers may be used.

Level 1. Do 4 to 6 repeats using 60-second rest intervals.

Level 2: Do 6 to 8 repeats using 60-second rest intervals.

Level 3: Do 8 to 12 repeats using 60-second rest intervals.

Position Weaknesses

Many players have decent overall skills, for the level of hockey they are playing. Many players also often have one major weakness that repeatedly makes a coach think, "If only . . .". Often these weaknesses can be improved by some specific aspect of conditioning. (Some skill weaknesses are mechanical in nature and do not relate to this discussion.) Drills for some of the more common position weaknesses that can be improved by conditioning are presented here.

Goaltenders

Developing goaltenders could often use conditioning to improve the explosive quickness in their legs in addition to maximizing hand quickness. Figure 8.9 illustrates an alactic leg drill that can be used by goalies. Figure 8.10 presents a sample hand quickness drill for goaltenders.

Figure 8.9
Leg quickness drill for goaltenders.

Goaltender hugs the right post with a shooter positioned to the left side of the net. The shooter slaps his stick on the ice, then immediately shoots on net. The goaltender must move rapidly across the crease to play the shot. Repeat drill working from other side of the net.

Figure 8.10
Hand quickness drill for goaltenders.

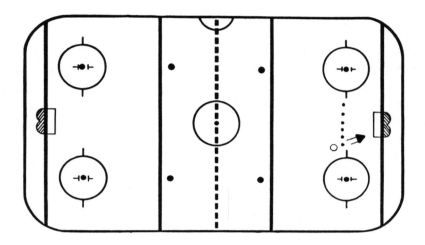

Goaltender assumes the proper stance in the middle of the crease. A shooter, positioned in the slot between the hash marks, fires 6 pucks as fast as possible, sending 3 to each glove. Rest. Repeat.

Level 1. Do the drill as described. Rest 30 to 60 seconds. Repeat 4 to 6 times.

Level 2. Use 8 to 10 pucks. Rest 30 to 60 seconds. Repeat 5 to 8 times.

Level 3. Use 10 to 12 pucks. Rest 30 to 60 seconds. Repeat 6 to 10 times.

Defensemen

Defensemen could often stand to improve the quickness of their feet and the overall strength of their bodies to be better at clearing the front of the net. Figure 8.11 illustrates a foot quickness drill for defensemen. Figure 8.12 provides a drill for developing overall body strength for the skills of working in front of the net.

Figure 8.11
"Quick feet" drill for defensemen.

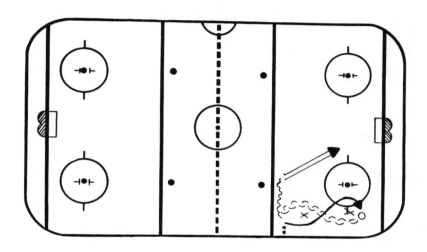

The defenseman starts on the blue line facing two pylons 1.5 to 2 meters (6 to 8 feet) from the boards. He skates all out in a figure-eight pattern through the pylons, going forward toward the end boards, backwards returning to the blue line where he picks up a puck, moves laterally toward center ice, and releases a shot on goal. Rest. Repeat.

Level 1. Do 4 to 6 repeats using 60-second rest intervals.

Level 2. Do 6 to 8 repeats using 60-second rest intervals.

Level 3. Do 8 to 12 repeats using 60-second rest intervals.

Figure 8.12
Body strength drill for defensemen.

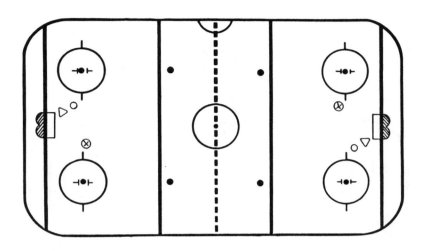

A forward stands in front of the net with his back to the net, in position to tip a shot. The defenseman stands between the forward and the net, facing the forward. On command, the defenseman tries to move the forward out of position as the forward tries to maintain his position. Work for 10 to 15 seconds. Rest. Repeat.

Level 1. Do 3 to 5 repeats using moderate resistance.

Level 2. Do 4 to 6 repeats using strong resistance.

Level 3. Do 6 to 8 repeats using determined resistance.

Centers

A centerman's value increases if he develops upper body quickness for taking faceoffs and if he develops a good backhand for passing and shooting. Both these skills have a strong conditioning component. Figure 8.13 presents a drill for working on faceoff quickness. Figure 8.14 is an alactic drill to improve backhand strength and quickness.

Figure 8.13
Faceoff quickness for centermen.

Centermen work in pairs. Use a third man to drop the puck. He has 5 to 10 pucks. As soon as the first faceoff puck has been cleared, the centers return to the set position and another puck is quickly dropped.

Level 1. Drop 5 pucks in succession. Rest. Repeat 3 to 5 times. Concentrate on technique.

Level 2. Drop 5 to 7 pucks in succession. Rest. Repeat 4 to 6 times. Concentrate on winning the faceoff.

Level 3. Drop 7 to 10 pucks in succession. Rest. Repeat 6 to 10 times. Do everything legal to win the faceoff.

Figure 8.14
Backhand strength drill for centermen.

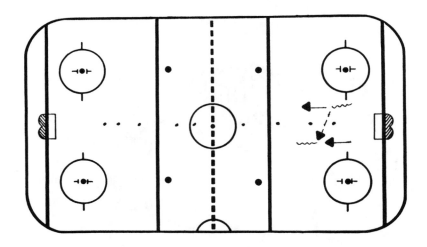

Place a row of pucks at irregular intervals down the length of the ice. Centerman starts at one end of ice flanked by a winger on his backhand side. Both players skate quickly down the ice with the winger slightly ahead of the center, as the center quickly passes each puck to his winger. Rest. Repeat.

Level 1. Center may use boards instead of a winger until his wrist strength improves. Then he can also work on accuracy. Use up to 6 pucks.

Level 2. Use 6 to 10 pucks.

Level 3. Use 8 to 12 pucks and concentrate on quickness of release and accuracy of the pass. Winger may vary his position relative to the centerman.

Wingers

Wingers are also more effective if they develop good wrist strength for shots and puck control. In addition, they need good breaking speed to maximize opportunities of driving for the net. Figure 8.15

provides a drill for developing wrist strength. Figure 8.16 is an acceleration drill for driving speed.

Figure 8.15
Wrist strength drill for wingers.

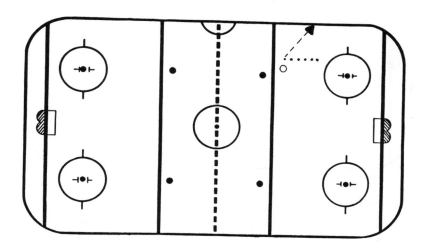

Use 6 to 10 weighted pucks, rocks, or small cans of cement and three different pass distances to a target. Player releases pucks in rapid succession at the target from the closest pass distance, using a forehand pass. Rest. Repeat drill using a backhand pass. Then repeat drill from the next nearest pass distance, and finally from the farthest pass distance. Do one set at the end of the complete drill using 6 normal pucks placed at close, medium, and long pass distances, alternating forehand and backhand passes. This set should be done nonstop while concentrating on accuracy.

Level 1. Use 6 weighted pucks and keep distances similar to what players would use in a game.

Level 2. Use 6 to 8 weighted pucks and a wider spread in distances.

Level 3. Use 8 to 10 weighted pucks and vary from short to very long pass distances.

Figure 8.16
Acceleration drill.

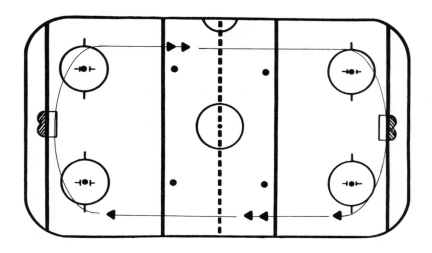

Players skate the perimeter of the ice. When they come to the first blue line, they break at full speed to the next blue line, then continue around the ice at a comfortable pace. When they come to the next blue line, they break over and back between the blue lines 3 times. Next time it is 5 times over and back, then 7, then 5, 3, and finally 1 again. Rest. Repeat. Change direction for each set.

Level 1. Do as described only once.

Level 2. Do as described 3 times. Use at least 2-minute rest intervals.

Level 3. Do as described but add a defensive player between the blue lines for the winger to try to beat. Repeat 3 to 5 times using 2-minute rests.

Many players exhibit some specific position weaknesses that can be improved by conditioning. These individuals could be given specific on-ice drills that meet the training principles for the element they are weak in. These can be done individually during the last 10 minutes of practice. Some of these same drills could be modified to be done on players' own time in a gym or paved driveway.

Summary

Players can get even more from a regular team conditioning program if they use a few additional training tips. Warm up properly before games and practices. Cool down after workouts and games. Combine training needs and skill work to get more time to work on all that needs to be done to improve your game. And do a little extra work on conditioning aspects that may be inhibiting the improvement of certain hockey skills. These small items can make a major difference in your game.

PART III

Designing Your Own Conditioning Programs

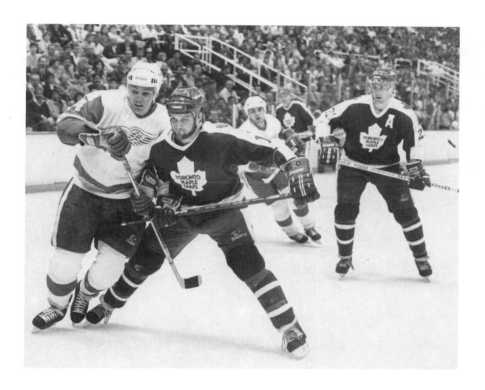

CHAPTER 9

Evaluating Progress

It is one thing to incorporate conditioning into your hockey program. But if you never evaluate it, you have little way of knowing whether or not your system is working as effectively as it could. To monitor improvement is one reason it is worth taking the time to do some fitness testing.

Another benefit of testing is that it provides targets to which players can aspire. If the players who never tire in a game can run 3,000 meters (2 miles) in 12 minutes, then perhaps that is a good target for all team members for aerobic conditioning. If results are kept year after year, they provide guidelines for future team targets as well.

When players are tested periodically, their results can be used as a base (normal) when illness or injury strikes. If a player's grip strength was known to be 65 kilograms before a wrist injury and 30 kilograms after, it is easy to tell how much retraining he needs and when he has returned to full strength after the injury.

Testing can also be used to diagnose a player's weaknesses. If a defenseman who has a poor slap shot is tested, results may show that he has poor shoulder flexibility. That factor alone can be developed to improve his slap shot. Testing can also diagnose team weaknesses, which can aid strategy decisions. Early in the season, testing may show that the team has a generally low aerobic fitness level. This means low endurance and poor recovery. This in turn means it would be smart to use short shifts and not to use a forechecking style of play, to keep team speed up longer into the game.

Testing provides warning signals when the season's training program is not working or when players are losing their level of conditioning. It may be because of too many games and no practices, or too long a layoff (e.g., Christmas vacation).

Testing can be conducted in a variety of ways. There are sports medicine clinics that specialize in testing athletes. They use expensive, state-of-the-art equipment and can provide very accurate measures of both muscle and energy supply status. However, for many teams and individual players, such laboratories may be inaccessible, too expensive, or ultimately impractical. For this reason, the focus of this section of the book is on "field testing."

Field tests are based on practical ways of estimating the level of a fitness component. These tests can be general (like a 12-minute run for an aerobic test) or sport specific (like a 60-second shuttle skate for an anaerobic lactic test). They must be carefully conducted to minimize inaccuracies in assessment, but if well designed, they can provide valuable information about a team's conditioning. Team members can be taught to test themselves or each other, which makes the test experience more practical and motivating.

Principles of Testing

The following principles must be incorporated to ensure that you are testing what you really want to test. The principles apply to on- or off-ice testing.

There are two key points to keep in mind when selecting your test items. First, make sure that each test item can be repeated exactly the same way each time the players repeat the test. You do not want results influenced by a change in technique rather than conditioning. For example, if you are using sit-ups as an abdominal muscle endurance test, either hold the feet or do not hold the feet every time you do the testing. That factor alone can change the results.

Second, in selecting a test item, be sure that skill is not a major factor. For example, if you use a shuttle skate as an anaerobic lactic test, do not include pucks because the skill of puckhandling becomes a major influence on the results. Remember that it is fitness you are trying to evaluate with these tests, not the skill level of a player. You can design skill tests as separate items if you wish to monitor skills improvement.

Muscle Strength/Endurance

To test muscle strength/endurance:

• Select an exercise that isolates a muscle group as much as possible and that requires minimal skill. For example, push-ups would be better than arm step-ups as an upper body strength/endurance test item.

• Perform the exercise either as often as possible in a set time limit, or at a specified pace until the player is too tired to keep the pace. For example, push-ups can be as many as a player can do in a minute, or they can be done at a pace of 50 per minute until the player drops off the pace.

• Include an exercise for each of the major muscle groups used in ice hockey (i.e., arm/shoulders, trunk, legs).

Sample Muscle Strength/Endurance Test Items.   Figure 9.1 illustrates three exercises that are often used to test shoulder, trunk, and leg strength/endurance. Note that explanations must be precise to keep tests consistent. Note also that these examples are tests of combination strength/endurance, not strength alone. Pure strength testing requires measurement of a single, maximal contraction, which requires specific equipment that is not suitable for field testing.

Figure 9.1
Muscle strength/endurance test items.

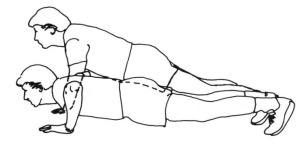

(a) Push-ups. One player places his fist on the floor under a partner's chest as he assumes the push-up position. Player lowers his whole body until his chest touches the partner's fist, then pushes back up until his elbows are extended. This counts as one push-up. The first player counts the total number of push-ups performed in 1 minute or in keeping with the set pace.

(b) Sit-ups. One player holds a partner's feet. Shoulder blades must touch the floor on every down position, hands are on the head, and elbows must touch the thighs on every up position. Partner counts the total number of sit-ups performed in 1 minute or in keeping with the set pace.

(c) Squat thrusts. Player starts in a position on all fours with the hands on the floor directly under the shoulders and the knees directly under the hips. A stick or line is placed immediately behind the toes. On a signal, the player moves to a tuck position so that the knees come inside and even with the elbows, then he extends the feet so that they land behind the stick. Then the player returns to the tuck position. A partner sits in line with the elbows so that he can coach completeness of the movements and count the correct squat thrusts that are completed in 1 minute or in keeping with a prescribed pace.

Flexibility

To test flexibility:

- Test one joint at a time while stabilizing all others.

- A preference is to work with gravity rather than against it.

- Flex to the farthest point possible and take the measurement while holding the position (do not bounce).

- Test each of the major joints needed in ice hockey (shoulders, hips, groin).

Sample Flexibility Test Items. Figure 9.2 illustrates common shoulder, hip, and groin tests. Note how the stretch can be measured precisely the same way (to the same point) each time it is tested so that changes in score are actually a result of flexibility, not measuring technique.

Figure 9.2
Flexibility test items.

(a) Sit-and-reach test. Player sits on the floor with legs straight and reaches slowly forward toward his feet. Measure the distance short of or beyond the bottom of the feet that the player is able to reach with his parallel fingertips.

(b) Shoulder flexibility test. The player should lie flat on the floor, face down, extend arms over head, and grasp a pencil in two fists. Keep the forehead on the floor and take the pencil as high up off the floor as possible. Keep the wrists straight. Measure the distance the pencil is above the floor.

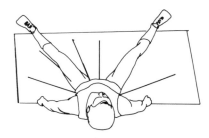

(c) Groin stretch test. Player lies back on the floor with his hips tight to the wall and his legs extended up the wall in a V shape. Relax the legs completely, letting them slide down the wall as far as possible. Measure the inside angle of the V formed by the legs. Draw the angle on the wall or on a large piece of bristol board ahead of time to make measuring easier.

Anaerobic Alactic Energy System

To test the anaerobic alactic energy system (quickness):

• Select a movement that can be performed absolutely "guts out."

• Duration can be either momentary, like a vertical jump, if you want to know a player's maximal output, or up to 10 seconds, if you want an indication of capacity.

Sample Quickness Tests.   An off-ice field test often used to determine explosive energy in the legs is a vertical jump. Players chalk their fingers and reach as high up the wall as possible, touching the wall to leave a mark. Then from a squat position, they jump to tag the wall as high as possible. The distance between the two chalk marks is recorded.

Because quickness is so specific in hockey, due to the mechanics of skating, an on-ice test is preferable when possible. Also, because quickness is often needed beyond a split second, alactic capacity is important. Figure 9.3 illustrates an on-ice quickness capacity test that is more specific to hockey. It looks at how effectively a player can explode three times in a row, an upper limit of what may happen in a game. The test requires use of an experienced person with a stopwatch. Ideally, electronic timing should be available.

Figure 9.3
On-ice quickness test.

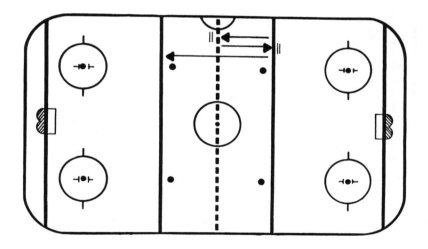

Player starts on the blue line facing the center line. On command the player skates to center, stops, returns to the blue line, stops, then skates past the center line. Skate is done as fast as possible with pinpoint starts and stops. Record time from the start until the player crosses the center line. If a player stumbles or falls during the test, give him a rest and retest.

Anaerobic Lactic Capacity

To test the anaerobic lactic capacity (speed):

• Select an activity that can be done as hard as possible for 60 to 90 seconds, like sprinting.

Sample Speed Tests.   Anaerobic lactic tests are difficult to perform. Players must go all out all the way through the test so that they are completely exhausted at the end and have not paced themselves. Tests can be done off-ice, like timing a 400-meter sprint. Again because of hockey's specificity, more useful information can be taken from an on-ice test. Figure 9.4 illustrates an on-ice speed test that provides a variety of lactic system information.

Figure 9.4
On-ice speed test.

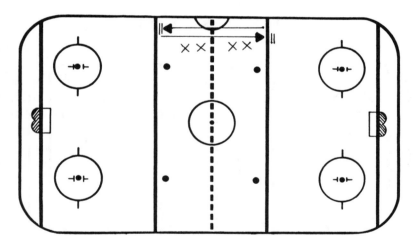

Divide the distance between the blue lines into five equal segments using pylons. Players work in pairs, with one player skating over and back from blue line to blue line as fast as possible. The other player counts the distance skated in 60 seconds. Record distance to tenths of a lap (over and back is one lap). The total distance only can be recorded or, as the timer calls elapsed time at 15, 30, 45, and 60 seconds, accumulated distance can be recorded. This provides information regarding dropoff times, which have implications for how long a player's speed lasts for him in a hard shift.

Aerobic Energy Supply System

To test the aerobic energy supply system:

• Use an activity that involves whole body exercise, such as running, biking, or skating.

• Perform the activity continuously for 12 minutes, if distance is to be recorded; if recovery heart rate is to be monitored, 6 minutes of activity is sufficient.

• Be sure that skill level and test conditions, such as weather or equipment, will have negligible influence on test results.

Sample Aerobic Tests.   A standard aerobic test is a 12-minute exercise test. This can be done off-ice or on-, although it may be more accurate done off-ice if the players usually run for aerobic conditioning. Players tend to coast too much in the on-ice version of the test, which throws off the results.

To conduct the test, divide the team into two groups. One group skates or runs laps while a partner in the other group records the distance covered in the 12 minutes. Record distance to the nearest 1/8 of a lap. Players must cover as much distance as possible in the 12 minutes. They should be exhausted at the end. They should be kept informed of the amount of time remaining throughout the exercise so they can judge their speed and are able to push to their maximum. Figure 9.5 illustrates how to set up the rink surface if this test is to be conducted on-ice. Start skaters at different points around the surface so they do not all get to the corners at the same time.

An alternative to the 12-minute test for aerobics is a heart rate recovery test. This is valuable for hockey players because recovery rate is so important during the game. This test can be done on-ice for more specificity. Players skate as strongly as possible for 6 minutes and particularly hard the last 2 minutes. Players must be practiced at taking 10-second heart rate counts (see chapter 7 aerobic training hints) or heart rate monitors must be available. As soon as the 6 minutes are up, a warning whistle blows for players to immediately stop skating and find their pulse. Five seconds later, the time keeper calls ''start'' and players count their pulse, beginning with 0, 1, 2 . . . At exactly 10 seconds, the time keeper calls ''stop.'' Record that 10-second pulse count (multiplied by 6). The warning, start, and stop procedure is repeated at 30 seconds after

Figure 9.5
On-ice aerobic test setup.

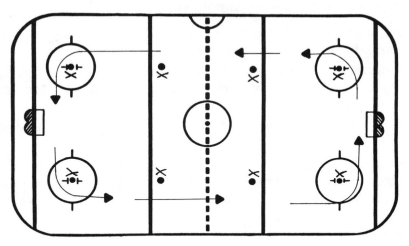

the skate, 60 seconds, 90 seconds, and 120 seconds. In 2 minutes of recovery, someone with an excellent aerobic system will have his heart rate return to less than 120 beats per minute from an exercise rate near 180. Players whose heart rates drop faster recover more quickly and can be used more frequently on shifts without tiring.

Below are hints regarding testing:

• Warm up before all tests.

• Ensure that items selected for testing minimize the influence of skill level or test technique on results.

• Pure strength tests are not presented here because they cannot be easily conducted as field tests. They require expensive equipment to test accurately. Functional strength tests (in the form of strength/ endurance), such as those suggested here, are more representative of the way strength is used in hockey.

• If a team does wish to invest in some strength testing equipment, the most affordable items would be a grip strength dynamometer (see Figure 9.6) and a leg strength dynamometer (see Figure 9.7). These items are sufficiently accurate to monitor the most important muscle groups for player strength. Teams who have access to good weight training equipment could be tested using the weights they have been training on, by finding the maximal weight they can lift completely for selected muscle groups.

Figure 9.6
Grip strength dynamometer.

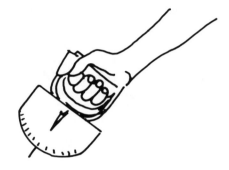

Figure 9.7
Leg strength dynamometer.

• Teams often wish to assess body composition because weight control, whether to add or delete, is important to a hockey player. He needs to know that the weight he is carrying is mostly functional (muscle) weight as opposed to excess baggage (fat). Weight can be monitored, but weight alone does not tell if changes are due to muscle acquisition, which is desirable, or fat, which is undesirable in most cases. Aside from the "pinch an inch" test, the least expensive, relatively accurate way of determining body composition is by using skinfold calipers, such as the type illustrated in Figure 9.8, to take measurements of folds of skin, which include the underlying fat. The sites used for these tests vary with age, sex, and even sport. It is important that measurements be taken by an experienced tester and that an established formula be used for determining percent body fat. Coaches are advised to consult with an experienced tester, often found at a university, YMCA/YWCA, or fitness center, to get access to the appropriate technology and norms for their teams.

Figure 9.8
Skinfold calipers.

• Fitness standards have not been provided in this presentation. Some figures are available for some of the tests, but many are from laboratory tests and are specific to how they were conducted. Teams are advised to develop their own standards over time.

• Testing is most useful if done at least twice a year. Pre-season testing shows where players are starting. Conditioning needs can be met early in the season and a base is established in case of injury. Mid-season testing shows how the conditioning program is holding up and allows time for topping up any factors that have slipped before the all important playoffs. Post-season testing is useful to check on maintenance and to evaluate the year's conditioning program. It also provides targets for players' off-season training programs.

Fitness Test Batteries

A team must decide how much time, money, and effort it wants to invest in testing and how much information it wants from testing. Then test items can be selected, and the overall fitness test battery can be designed.

When the test items have been selected, they must be placed in an order that does not allow one test to throw off the results of another. For example, doing skinfold caliper measurements after a 12-minute aerobic test would make the caliper measurements inaccurate due to the sweat along the skin (water under the skin). Similarly, an aerobic test done following a speed test would likely make the aerobic results lower because players would have a lactate buildup from the speed test, and heart rate would already be high.

If a complete test battery is done, skinfolds and weight are usually tested first. Aerobics and speed are usually tested on separate days and as the last item of the day. Other items come between and can be spread over the 2 days.

Figure 9.9 presents an example of a record sheet used to monitor results of a player's fitness tests. This test battery was designed according to one particular team's and coach's time, equipment, and needs. You may use different test items and have other priorities regarding what to include or omit. The items were tested over 2 days in the following order:

Day 1. (*Off-ice, before practice*) weight, skinfolds, strength/
endurance tests
(*On-ice, beginning of practice*) 6-min. heart rate recovery
test

Day 2. (*Off-ice, before practice*) strength dynamometers, flexibility
(*On-ice, beginning of practice*) quickness, speed

Figure 9.9
Fitness appraisal record.

Name _____   Birthdate _____

Season: Pre   Mid   Post

Date:

Body composition
  Wt (kg/lb)
  % Body fat
Muscle ability
  Push-ups/min
  Sit-ups/min
  Right grip (kg/lb)
  Left grip (kg/lb)
  Legs (kg/lb)
Flexibility
  Hip (cm/in.)
  Shoulder (cm/in.)
  Groin (°)
Energy supplies
  Quickness (sec)
  Speed (laps @)
    15 sec
    30 sec
    45 sec
    60 sec
  Aerobic (HR @)
    Start
    30 sec
    60 sec
    90 sec
    120 sec

Summary

Fitness testing provides some valuable information for a hockey player and coach. Testing does not have to be expensive or very time-consuming if field tests are used. However, tests must meet specific criteria to be accurate. Players can be taught how to do many field tests for themselves, which provides more motivation for conditioning.

CHAPTER 10

Planning Your Season

This book has presented information on conditioning muscles and energy supply systems and looked at ways to assess the effectiveness of the program. The challenge is how to build all that information into a team's hockey season. Few schedules and facilities provide ideal conditions for doing all the conditioning that it would be nice to do.

The best way to get the most out of what a team has to work with is to design a master plan before the year begins. Take into account the limitations that must be accommodated and the goals that the team wants to reach.

Following is a step-by-step approach to help a coach or player establish an effective season's plan for a team or individual. The steps are presented from the coach and team perspective.

Step 1. Establish Your Starting Point

Sit down with pen and paper in hand and make notes in response to the following questions.

- What ages are the players?
- What hockey experience do they have? Skill levels?
- What conditioning experience and interest do they have?
- How many weeks in the whole season?
- What lengths are the season segments? Pre-season? In-season? Playoffs? Off-season?
- What key dates have to be accommodated during the season? During tournaments? During layoffs?

- How many practices do we have per week?
- How many games per week?
- How much time per practice can be devoted to conditioning?
- What equipment do we have to work with? What facilities?
- Will I have an assistant coach? Conditioning consultant?
- Is it possible to do off-ice conditioning?

The picture painted by the responses to the above questions will change year to year. They should indicate the realistic limitations and possibilities that you have to work with to manage a conditioning program for the team. Some conditioning is possible in all situations, although it is certainly easier to work into some situations than others.

A team that practices three times a week in a rink adjacent to an indoor track facility and that can afford to hire a fitness consultant will have an easier time of conducting a good conditioning program than a team that has 1 hour per week to practice and play and a coach who has to do everything himself. But both can design good conditioning programs with careful planning. In other words, there really is no excuse for lack of conditioning in a hockey team.

Step 2. Testing

Conduct fitness tests (as discussed in chapter 9) as soon as possible. These tests can be as elaborate or as simple as you and your assistants have the time and expertise to manage. Tests done at this time will show what the conditioning needs of the team are and what individuals have particular weaknesses that should be improved. These tests also let a coach know what he can and cannot expect from members of the team in the early going of the season, which has implications for strategies he can apply successfully. For example, if the team generally is in poor aerobic and anaerobic shape, he may be well advised to employ a short shift strategy until they improve because longer shifts will result in greater accumulation of lactic acid which will ruin their speed partway through a period. They will last longer at their top speeds if lactate is not allowed to build up too much on each shift.

Testing provides more information on team needs and limitations, which should likely be accommodated in a season's plan.

Step 3. Set Season Objectives

Once you know what you have to work with and where you are starting regarding conditioning, you are ready to determine your team's objectives for the season; these will include specific objectives for individual players, because the players are not likely to be all at the same level. These objectives should be set for segments of the season as well as overall.

For example, if you have two or three practices a week and a team that has done conditioning before, you should be able to set a goal of about 6 weeks for being ready to switch to maintenance frequencies for most conditioning factors. Some players may need specific individual objectives at this time as well. For example, a couple of players may be particularly slow, so a 10% improvement in quickness may be an additional 6-week goal for them.

Maintenance would be the main objective for the next part of the season and should be checked by testing. A second objective during the maintenance period may be continued quickness improvement for the whole team, because you want to have exceptional speed by playoff time.

An objective for the end of the season may be to have no loss in any aspect of conditioning from the levels established at the end of the first 6-week period.

If a team only gets to practice once a week, these objectives would be unrealistic, but others, like improving aerobics, quickness, and flexibility all season long, may be more appropriate. This would likely be the case with young players who are growing and who are involved in other sports besides hockey.

Objectives should be periodically reassessed to ensure that they are realistic yet set sufficient challenge that conditioning is not lost during the season. They may need to be readjusted during a season. Follow-up testing is the soundest way of verifying whether or not the conditioning objectives are being met.

Step 4. Design the Season's Conditioning Program

This is the point at which you sit down and tape three items on the bulletin board in front of you: the limitations and opportunities

(Step 1 and 2), the objectives (Step 3), and a chart containing the principles for training each conditioning component discussed in chapters 4 to 7.

Figure 10.1 illustrates some headings you may want to use in your *Principles of Training* chart. Note that the *Principles* and *Maintenance Frequency* columns will be the same for everyone. But the other three columns will depend partly on information from Steps 1 and 2. For example, if the players are in good shape, time to improve will be less than if they are in poor shape going into the season. A mite team may have to do aerobic training in season, whereas a junior team should do most of its aerobic training in the off-season.

Figure 10.1
Sample principles of training chart.

	Principles	Time to improve	Season	Maintenance frequency	Season
Strength/ endurance					
Flexibility					
Quickness					
Speed					
Aerobics					

Make up an overall calendar for your season, such as the one illustrated in Figure 10.2. A day-by-day calendar is necessary later when actual practice plans are designed. This season calendar can also include columns for skills and one for strategy planning if you wish to coordinate your whole hockey plan.

Figure 10.2
Season plan calendar.

Week/season dates	No. of practices	No. of games	Conditioning (practice no.)				
			Str/end	Flex	Speed	Quick	Aerob
1/ Pre. Seas. 10/3-9	4	0	1-4 off-ice	daily	2&4 on-ice	1-4 on-ice	1&3 on-ice 2&4 off-ice
2/ Pre. 10/10-16	2	2 Exhib.	1&2 off-ice	daily	1&2 *emphasize	1&3	1&2 off-ice
3/ Early Season 10/17-23	3	1	3 off-ice 1 on-ice	daily	1&2 on-ice	2&2 on-ice	2 off-ice 3 on-ice
4/ Early 10/24-30	2	2	1&2 off-ice	daily	1&2 on-ice	1&2	1&2 off-ice
5/ Early 10/31-11/6	3	1	Same as week #3				
6/ Mid Season 11/20-27	2	2	1 off-ice	daily	1 on-ice	2 on-ice	2 on-ice

Objectives
* Begin maintenance of aerobics and strength/endurance
△ Begin maintenance of speed and quickness

First, slot in games and any layoffs. Next, mark the dates by which certain objectives should be reached. Then put in the type of exercise or drill that should be included in each practice to meet the training principles, objectives, and limitations you have in front of you. At this time, you do not have to list the precise drill you will use, but defining what you are trying to accomplish is important. For example, you may need a circuit that lasts 20 minutes for the February 23rd practice. Time is of the essence with playoffs approaching. With only one practice that week, due to two games, an aerobics, muscle endurance, and quickness maintenance session is needed that practice. A circuit is a quick way to meet all three needs. You can slot in the exact exercises on your day calendar in February when you know better which muscles need most work.

Having a season's log like this allows a coach to sit down and see when it is possible to slot in special conditioning sessions for individual weaknesses that arise as the season progresses. For example, a coach may see that a defenseman who has returned from an injury has really slowed down in his footwork. A look at the season's plan will show a week coming up where there is only one game, so in the three practices leading up to that game, this individual could be worked a little harder than usual on his explosive power to get him caught up again.

Set up a master plan using your limitations, objectives, and the principles of training so that you can see at a glance where the loopholes are and where modifications can easily be made. This way, there is nothing that is left out or that cannot be accommodated somehow.

Once you have designed the season's plan, use it. It's not just an exercise to make you think. At the beginning of each month or each change in season, fill in your day plan with more detail of specific drills. Many coaches find it valuable to leave space for comments in the day plan, at the end of each week or session. Coaches keep these plans from year to year and refer to them when they plan the next season. The comments remind the coach of what worked and what was not so impressive. That way he knows better and better what will be successful for him as time goes on.

Step 5. Retest and Reevaluate

A couple of times should be set aside during the season to retest the conditioning level of the players and for the coach to consider if anything is missing or could be improved. Mid-season is one useful time, and a couple of weeks before playoffs is another, because then there is still time to make adjustments if necessary. Just because you made a seasonal plan does not guarantee that it will be as successful as you hope. Test it, and ask yourself if there is anything you could do better. If there is, make the adjustments in your plan and record your reasons under "comments" for future reference.

Winning may not be everything, but being the best that you can be certainly counts for something.

Summary

Sit down and plan your season from the outset. A step-by-step approach helps ensure that conditioning needs are met within the limitations imposed by your team's situation. Objectives can be clearly established and the likelihood of overlooking something useful is reduced. The plan also makes it easier to work in modifications and special sessions when necessary. The team does better, and the coach feels satisfied with his efforts when the season ends.

Legend

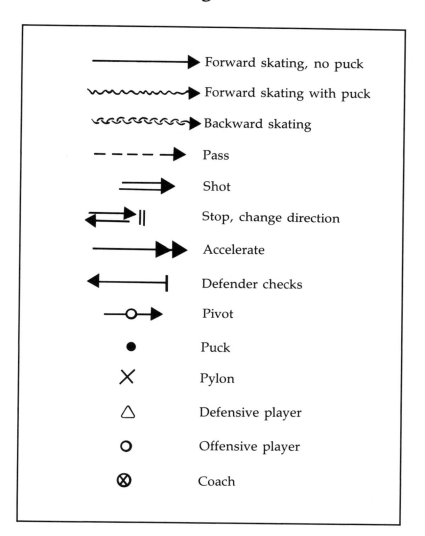

Forward skating, no puck

Forward skating with puck

Backward skating

Pass

Shot

Stop, change direction

Accelerate

Defender checks

Pivot

Puck

Pylon

Defensive player

Offensive player

Coach

About the Authors

Don MacAdam is head coach for the Edmonton Oilers Development Team in the American Hockey League and coauthor of two other books, *The Hockey Conditioning Handbook* and *How to Make the Best Use of Your Ice Time*. Before joining the Oilers, MacAdam played professional ice hockey for several years and coached for more than 15 years at both university and professional levels. He was named Atlantic Universities Athletic Association  Coach of the Year in 1984 and lectures at hockey clinics throughout Canada and the United States. Don earned his masters in physical education from the University of New Brunswick.

Gail Reynolds runs her own fitness consulting company and is author of *Look at You: A Fitness Approach* and coauthor of *The Hockey Conditioning Handbook* and *How to Make the Best Use of Your Ice Time*. *Coaching Review* has published two of her articles: "Check Their Pulse" and "Uses and Abuses of Flexibility." She has spoken at several Canadian Amateur Hockey Association Level 4 and 5 clinics and lectured at the York Symposium for Elite Coaches. Gail earned her masters in physical education from the University of Western Ontario, where she specialized in exercise physiology and psychology.